CHOOSING JOY

HAPPY SUN
ADY BERGER
JAN 1, 2011

CHOOSING JOY

Alzheimer's: A Book of Hope

Helene Berger

REIBERG PRESS
2019

Published by Reiberg Press
www.HeleneBerger.com

All information, content, and material in this book is for informational purposes only and is not intended as a substitute for consultation with and/or medical treatment by a qualified physician or healthcare provider. The reader should regularly consult a physician in matters relating to his/her health and particularly with respect to any symptoms that may require diagnosis or medical attention.

Book design by Steve Dyer
Cover design by P. R. Brown, Bau-Da

ISBN: 978-0-578-45072-8 (print)
ISBN: 978-0-578-45073-5 (e-book)

Printed in the United States of America

Dedicated, in loving memory,
to my husband

ADOLPH J. (ADY) BERGER

a gentle, kind, pure, and ethical man
who encouraged me to live fully
and faced the changes of his final years
with extraordinary grace and courage

When it rains it pours.
Maybe the art of life is to convert
tough times to great experiences:
we can choose to hate the rain
or dance in it.

—JOAN MARQUES

CONTENTS

Part One: Foundations

Part Two: Practical Approaches

PART ONE

FOUNDATIONS

4/4/2010

CHAPTER ONE

A Role You Did Not Choose

We spend most of our lives preparing for the future we envisioned for ourselves. We might work hard to get into a good college or train to excel in a sport we choose. We prepare as diligently as we can for the profession we seek. We read books on marriage and parenting.

Then, sometimes right at the time when we feel we have achieved our life's goals, when we have fulfilled our responsibilities to children and profession and are looking forward to winding down and savoring the time to pursue other interests, we are caught off guard with a doctor's proclamation: "You have Alzheimer's"—or Parkinson's, or a cancer, or a critical heart or lung condition, or another life-threatening disease; a brief sentence that brings our carefully crafted world crashing down and changes our lives forever.

When we first received the diagnosis of Alzheimer's, my husband was about to retire. Our children were well-established in their careers and each of our grandchildren seemed solid and full of potential. We had hoped to have the leisure time to travel and enjoy each other. The years ahead were ones we had worked a lifetime to enjoy. Now three words had changed everything.

Too often, no matter how conscientious we have been in previous roles in our lives, we slide into what may be our most challenging responsibility yet with no plan or direction, unprepared and ill-equipped for this unanticipated transition. This verdict was not in our life's plan. We dread going through this new doorway. We don't have confidence in ourselves. We fear being in a place where we have no command and no control.

Most of us tumble into this new caregiving role without acknowledging to ourselves what a momentous transformation has just taken place, not only for our afflicted mate or loved one but for ourselves. Faced with the need for immediate action, we shoot from the hip. We try to handle the change without reevaluating, without a plan, without knowing our options. Our world has just taken a major turn, one we are woefully unprepared to deal with, yet we don't understand what a steep and crucial learning curve lies before us. So it is vital here, too, just as in our younger days, to educate ourselves about this new and unanticipated reality. Too often, by the time we begin to learn what might have worked, the negative consequences of this unwelcome sentence have become so entrenched that they are difficult or impossible to change.

In this book, I describe all that I learned during my husband's last six years, in the hope that it will make others' paths easier, calmer, less stressful—and, yes, happier. I knew I was not prepared for what I was facing, but it took me several years to comprehend the enormity of the transition I had to make. Gradually, I understood that I could no longer get by on instinct, that this was not the time to merely react in the moment to day-to-day challenges. That this was another life opportunity to learn and to grow—to learn that we *always* have options, even if it's only the attitude we bring to conditions that we would do anything to change.

I realized that I could not just continue to react in a haphazard way. I had to consciously change my world and that of my husband. I had to become the manager of a huge new enterprise, tackling my new role as if I had just been hired to run a major company. I set out to observe and learn all that I could to make our lives as fulfilling as possible, for as long as possible, given our new constraints. As the years went on, I began to pay constant attention to what worked and what did not. In the process, I discovered many positive techniques that I write about in these pages.

For example, I began to include Ady in all the decision-making that affected him. Instead of telling him what had to be done, I asked him—often giving several choices, each of which was acceptable. He made the decisions, he owned the decisions, and, most importantly, he accepted them without argument or frustration. In more difficult situations, when Ady expressed genuine opposition, we worked out the differences together, trying to avoid confrontation. Increasingly, he was the one to come up with the solution. Instead of bucking each other, pulling in opposite directions, we became a team working towards a common goal.

Perhaps the most essential change that I consciously made was in my perspective. If we, our loved ones' caregivers, feel frustrated, disappointed, sad, or angry about the new role foisted upon us, those feelings are magnified many times over for our patients. They didn't choose this either. The more compassion, kindness, tenderness, and love we can offer, the easier life will be for both. A brain blocked by anger and frustration cannot function at an optimal level. A peaceful, predictable, non-combative environment creates the opportunity for inner calm and healing. At first, I had to remind myself constantly of this approach, but over time it became easier and eventually almost instinctive. The more I gave genuine praise and encouragement, the more the typical frustration vanished.

If I ever got frustrated I would think back to advice I was given many years earlier, advice that has always stayed with me and sustained me throughout these complicated years. It was 1987, and I was the incoming national chair of a major organization.

As I was about to accept the leadership role, I asked my predecessor for guidance. She unwittingly gave me the best advice I could have received. She was a bright and capable woman, but her response to me was, "I'm the wrong one to ask. I was starting my new business and didn't have time to give it my all. I wish I could do it over again."

I never forgot the pathos of those words. There are some things in life you don't get to do over. As it turned out, during the early months of my term of office, we moved into an apartment after twenty-nine years in our home, and my husband had a near-fatal bicycle accident and was hospitalized for many weeks, with many complications.

It would have been legitimate, and so much easier for me, to drop the ball with my chairmanship. But I pushed on, knowing that I would only hold this position for two years. I wouldn't get to do it again. I didn't ever want to look back and think *I wish I had . . .* Years later, with the signs of Ady's growing decline, how much greater a time in my life for me to say, "I will not leave a stone unturned. I don't ever want to look back and think, *If only I had . . .*" The reality is that the devotion and energy I put into my role as a caregiver has been the most demanding, yes, but also the most rewarding of my life.

The success Ady and I achieved together was far beyond anything that I could have envisioned. My life became easier, and his flourished. It was a classic win-win situation. Our lives evolved from bearable to pleasurable. So simple, once one develops the habit, and so marvelously productive!

This totally unanticipated outcome is what motivated me to gather all of the notes I had scribbled on the back of envelopes and on the blank pages of concert programs to try to understand what we did together that worked successfully. My goal is to give hope and offer concrete suggestions to others who have received that devastating pronouncement. While much of what I suggest are concrete ways to deal with medications, doctors, aides, time management, and decisions, the greater part of this book emphasizes the attitude that we bring to our spouse or loved one. No matter what the relationship was before the onset of any decline, the more we bring large doses of compassion, kindness, tenderness, support, and encouragement, the easier the path will be for both caregiver and patient. *Even if your past relationship was not ideal,* it's not too late to build a more supportive one.

Though the personal experience on which this book is based was with a loved one with Alzheimer's, it became clear as I wrote that many of the lessons learned and the insights gained could apply to a family member or patient who is declining for any reason—whether the affliction is Alzheimer's, Parkinson's, cancer, a chronic case of sciatica or back pain, or any other debilitating condition. In each case, the awareness of loss of function, dignity, health, self-respect, or zest for life can be devastating. The theme that echoes throughout this book is that our role as caregivers can have a profound impact—on the patient's psyche and willingness to cooperate, on their physical health and well-being, and on the life that patient and caregiver have together.

. . .

Important Caveat: I in no way wish to imply that a caregiver who follows the course of action suggested here will have similar success. Every person, every case, is unique. Countless deeply caring spouses have given love and devotion beyond measure and still ended up with a loved one who doesn't recognize them or becomes angry and abusive. I cannot offer any guarantee of a different outcome. Relationships come with a history—a history that shapes reactions to each other and to difficult situations. Regardless of your relationship, however, I believe that the evolving methodology described throughout this book has the potential to benefit both patient and caregiver, especially if introduced before unwanted behavior becomes habit.

This book attempts to suggest a path that might make the journey more tolerable for both patient and caregiver. I hope to inspire and empower you, the caregiver, with the knowledge that you are not helpless. You *can* make a difference. You can continue to open doors, rather than just witness them closing. You can increase the chances of success by providing mental stimulation; by encouraging creativity; by refraining from judgment or criticism; by giving support, appreciation, praise, and respect; and by remembering always the person your loved one once was and giving him or her the dignity they have earned throughout their lives. I hope to demonstrate that even during this overwhelmingly sad time, you and your loved one can choose to live with JOY.

CHAPTER TWO

Choosing Joy

MY HUSBAND, ADY BERGER, DIED ON MARCH 25, 2011, six years after being diagnosed with Alzheimer's disease. A stomach bug, not Alzheimer's, caused his death. Earlier that night, we had hosted a group of friends for dinner as a "thank-you" for their constant kindness, attentiveness, and support. Ady greeted all seventeen people at that table by name. Sitting at the head of the long table in his wheelchair, he suddenly, to my utter surprise, raised his glass (water for him; he never drank) and, with a big smile, welcomed the group with a spontaneous, loving, and coherent toast of appreciation. As we were leaving the restaurant, two of our close friends asked the same question, in the same words:

"Are you *sure* Ady has Alzheimer's?"

The following morning Ady did not wake up.

. . .

Six years earlier, Dr. Ranjan Duara, head of the outstanding Wien Center for Alzheimer's Disease and Memory Disorders in Miami, pronounced the definitive diagnosis. A series of tests confirmed what I had feared for some years: that Ady had Alzheimer's. After giving us a few minutes to digest the news, Dr. Duara turned to

Ady and asked, "How do you feel?" I listened in horror as my gentle, accomplished husband of over fifty years said flatly, "I don't want to live anymore."

And yet, over the next six years, Ady gradually regained the radiant smile he was known for. Throughout the last two to three years, he was able to do what had been unthinkable a few years earlier. As Dr. Duara explained, a brain is capable of building new passages around damaged ones. Ady had stopped playing the piano several years before. Now he resumed playing an hour every day—Mozart, Beethoven, Brahms, Rachmaninoff—playing from the scores of his vast repertoire. I tried to introduce Sudoku during the first three years, knowing his fascination with math. I thought he'd be a natural at it, but he was mystified by the puzzle and unable to grasp how to place all those numbers in the little squares. When I introduced Sudoku again several years later, he took to it immediately, and with me by his side, solved Sudoku problems almost nightly. He drew pictures for the first time in his life, pictures whose colorful lines were wavering and hesitant but whose subjects were varied and consistently joyful. He wrote nightly love letters to me with a clear hand—again, for the first time in his life. His progress was shockingly different from what one would expect from an Alzheimer's patient: the anger, impatience, temper, depression—even violence—that the doctors and nurses, in their efforts to be kind, tried to prepare me for.

. . .

This book chronicles HOW and WHY this regeneration was possible. Virtually every book about Alzheimer's, often by a spouse who suffered through their loved one's decline, is a litany of graphic horrors. This is a book of HOPE. It is a rare success story. It offers strategies for finding joy in your day-to-day life with an Alzheimer's patient even during this difficult time. It is the personal journey of one unprepared woman, neither a doctor nor an expert, who lived through these years by creating positive ways

to cope. It is the story of a wife who was determined to create a supportive environment for her husband—never dreaming the resiliency he ultimately displayed was possible. It chronicles my real-life experiences: the tears, the frustration, the uncertainty, the many mistakes, as well as the successes that enabled my husband to beat the odds of this dreaded disease.

I began this book unwittingly, with the journal I kept from the day of his diagnosis. During the next six years, my journal became my guide, reminding me of what worked and what didn't, what helped and what was detrimental. Once I wrote it down in black and white, I had a prescription for how I would react in the future. Only several years after Ady's passing, when I kept getting calls for guidance from those who had witnessed his miraculous progress, did I begin to understand I had the raw material for a book that might offer valuable guidance and hope to others.

. . .

My first journal entry described a day back in October, 2005, immediately following my husband's diagnosis of Alzheimer's. I sat at the Wien Center in a drab waiting room with a long string of attached chairs. The bare space was adorned only by two framed eight-by-ten photos of boats on the wall. Ady was about to participate in a research study. I had been handed voluminous forms to fill out. The bulk of the pages asked for my perception of my husband's abilities: was he able to drive, shop, cook, select clothes, handle personal hygiene, and handle financial matters? The final two pages dealt with the caregiver—me. How was I coping? How was I reacting to the changes in our lives?

I was asked to respond to a form with multiple-choice questions, each with five choices:

(1) Never
(2) Once a week
(3) Two to three times a week
(4) Four to six times a week
(5) Every day

The first question was, "How many times a week do you feel happy?"

My answer was immediate: "Every day."

Next question: "How many times a week do you feel sad?"

Again, my answer was immediate: "Every day."

There it was, in black and white. It was nothing I didn't know, yet it hit me like a thunderbolt. My answers seemed so contradictory, but they were both accurate. How can you be partners with a man for over fifty years, since you were married at age nineteen, and not feel an almost constant sadness when you see him slipping away from you? Tears seemed to fill my entire body. Yet I was simultaneously aware that the joyous spirit that had carried me throughout my life was with me still. I vowed to try to keep that spirit alive.

I began to understand my dual mission. The first was about Ady: to do everything in my power to slow the process of decline and give my husband the greatest fullness of life. At the same time,

I had to seek joy every day. I have lived an extraordinarily blessed and busy life. This was not the time to shut down. Letting the sadness quotient win would not be good for me, and it certainly would not be good for Ady.

The difference was this: All my life that joy had come naturally. Now I had to seek it.

Understanding this mission was amazingly liberating. Ady's care and well-being remained my main priority, but it was not my *only* priority. I had to continue to live fully. I gave myself permission to play tennis, to go to theater, to be with friends, to continue with some of my gratifying and fulfilling communal and national work. I gave myself permission to laugh, to have fun. I chose joy over sadness. None of our lives are free of pain and problems. But we can choose to live as fully and happily as our health and outlook allows, and this I was determined to do.

. . .

What I had no way of knowing, in those early days, was that the real joy would come not from external sources filling my life with happy experiences, but from within. It came through learning—through trial and error, through openness in observing what worked and what didn't, through an increasing sensitivity to how every approach or action or even body language on my part could either diminish Ady or support him. I found joy through helping my husband continue to live a full and happy life, with dignity and with that radiant Ady smile, feeling loved, appreciated, and respected.

Most of all, my joy came from the transformation that would unfold during the next six years. As sweet and gentle as Ady was, he exhibited clear tendencies in the earlier years of his illness that pointed in another direction: stubbornness, frustration, irritability, rigidity, annoyance (if not anger), occasionally even highly inappropriate behavior. These new tendencies frightened me. Yet all of this new and negative behavior, instead of becoming more entrenched, vanished by the end of the second or third year. Instead of sinking ever lower during his last years, he continued to improve in countless ways. These improvements were reflected not only in my own observation but in Ady's regular evaluations. I had no idea such regeneration was possible. I could not envision that with constant stimulation, support, and love, the brain is capable of making new passages around the damaged tissues. Four months before Ady passed away so unexpectedly, I asked Dr. Duara, who had reviewed both the surprising testing results and witnessed Ady in action, if such regeneration were possible. His response was swift: "Absolutely!"

I began to understand that the journey was mine as much as my husband's. I rarely lived with anger, and I did not want to turn into a woman consumed by inner rage at this stage of life. I had to fight the natural instinctive questions: "Why me? Why us? It isn't right! It isn't fair!!" I had to fight the many outrageous indignities, the demands on my time, my patience, my life. I read stacks of books on the Holocaust. Friends would tell me, "You should be reading stuff that's fun and uplifting." My response was that reading what real suffering was gave me perspective. It reinforced the knowledge that my life had been and still was uniquely blessed.

The discovery I never anticipated during those six years was not just how to bring out the best in someone with Alzheimer's or even how to enhance the life of a person who is declining in any way. It was how to better respond to *all* the people who matter in my life. I became more willing to listen; to walk in another's shoes; to express appreciation; to show respect; to acknowledge, support, and praise positive behavior. I learned that I didn't have all the answers, that I could withhold my opinion on occasion. I learned to be more sensitive to what someone needed from me; to remember what a diminished person had achieved in his or her prime; to provide the same kind of nurturing environment for the adults in my life as I would to help a child grow. I would not have chosen to learn these lessons in the way that I did. But they have deeply enhanced my own life and relationships. Not a bad prescription for life!

The simple strategies and approaches I impart throughout these pages made the last six years of Ady's life a happy and fulfilling time for both of us. I learned that together we could, in the words of a prayer from the Jewish Days of Awe, "avert the severe decree." I learned that it is possible to create the conditions that encourage regeneration, happiness, and growth. I learned to live with hope.

I learned that my job was to make sure that the joy quotient outweighed the sad every day, for each of us. I suspect that to live a full and happy life we have to consciously work to achieve balance. It's not a challenge to be happy when everything is going well. The challenge is to be happy despite elements in life that we would not have chosen. Early on in that waiting room, I began to recognize that both joy and sadness can and do exist inside us at the same time. As the poet William Blake wrote, "Joy and woe are woven fine." The goal is to keep joy the winner.

CHAPTER THREE

Remembering Yourselves: A Personal History

A DIAGNOSIS OF ALZHEIMER'S, OR ANY OTHER DEBILITATING disease, means that you and your loved one are about to embark on a new and unexpected journey. In preparation for your new role, as parts of the person you knew begin to slip away, it might be helpful in difficult moments to remember who your loved one was—and who you were—before the decline began. Remember the high points in your lives or thoughts that made you proud. Take stock of the personal qualities you bring to this journey. What do you each excel at? What are your strengths? How have you each used those strengths in your lives so far? What inner resources can you call upon in grappling with the many unexpected difficulties that will surely arise in the years ahead? Whom can you turn to for comfort, consolation, or guidance? *No* situation is typical. Both you and your loved one bring your own unique personality, temperament, and history to this new stage in your lives.

Here is a little of Ady's and my story.

Who Was Ady?

Ady and I met on Labor Day weekend at a beach vacation spot in Long Island. He had already completed five years at Dartmouth, where he received his B.A. and a double master's degree in engineering and business administration. He had been on the Dartmouth swimming team and sang in the Dartmouth glee club. He had served in the U.S. Air Force as a second lieutenant, then worked briefly in his father's silk mill business and as an engineer at Curtiss-Wright.

I was there with my family, about to transfer from two years at Cornell to Barnard College in New York. I had just completed eight intense weeks of Summer Stock at the Tufts Arena Theater and wanted only to sit at the pool to read and relax. My always observant mother came to me and said, "That nice young man keeps coming over to talk to you, and you're not giving him the time of day." She decided to invite Ady to lunch. During the meal,

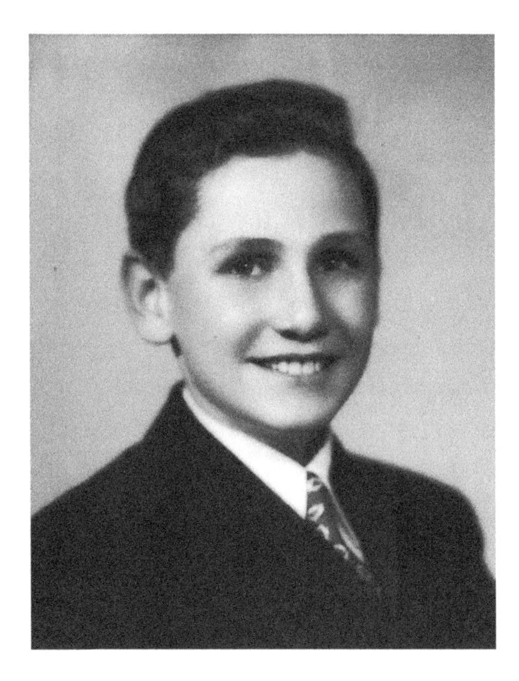

Ady, age 13

after a touching exchange between my family and me, I looked up and noticed a warm smile on Ady's face. I always suspected that was the first moment when he wanted to be part of our family. A few weeks later Ady came to our home and began playing the piano while waiting for me to appear. My mother was enthralled. I used to tease Ady, telling him that my mother fell in love with him before I did.

A few months later, we were engaged. I brought Ady with me for a special weekend at Cornell and proudly introduced my fiancé at the sorority house. A friend asked, "How do you know? How do you know this is the man you want to spend the rest of your life with?" The response I gave felt woefully inadequate. I could have said. "He's bright. He has rare integrity. He loves music. He's a great dancer. We have a lot in common," and a host of other important qualities. Instead I said just two words: "He's GOOD." Later I questioned myself: *If that's all you can say, why are you marrying this*

Ady in the U.S. Air Force

man? It took me years to understand that my original response was right on target.

Ady had many other important qualities that I didn't recognize when we were engaged. (We truly knew quite little about each other, and it was either pure luck or instinct or hard work, or all combined, that made the marriage a good one.) His engineering and business degrees suited his concrete and rational mind. His precision, at times, exasperated me. In the first year of our marriage, when working for a large company where his mind was not challenged, he kept a chart in our apartment of when the light bulbs blew out. If the check book did not balance by a nickel, he would literally spend hours until he found the error. If I expressed that there were better ways to spend his time, he explained that it could be two large errors that were offsetting each other. But that same rational mind made him love math and music and enabled him to play the piano beautifully, become a first-rate chess player, and be totally dependable.

He instinctively dealt superbly well with people. He was kind and patient and, as one of the many beautiful condolence letters I received after his passing said, "He treated the fanciest person and the menial worker with the same kindness and respect. In an age when people are too busy and rushed to care about others, Ady Berger was an anomaly." He was the most patient and supportive teacher and always felt that was his true calling. He never told his family or his staff what to do. Rather, he helped us figure it out ourselves. I believe these qualities made him not only successful later on in business, but made every worker who crossed his path, whether at the top echelon or a laborer, respect, admire, and trust him.

Who Am I?

If I were asked to name the quality that most defines me, it would be that I have a great zest for life and a vast appreciation for how blessed my life has been. I grew up in a loving home. My mother taught English in high school and would come home from teaching her honors classes flying with the insights she learned from her students. After leaving her teaching profession, she began to take on a leadership position in the local chapter of a national organization, which flourished under her direction.

My father was a dentist, beloved by his patients. He enjoyed research and was always ahead of his time with his own inventions and the latest gadgets. He had courted my mother by reading poetry. No matter what the conversation at dinner, he usually managed to jump up and get his yellowed and worn copy of *The Book of English Verse,* saying, with a smile, "That reminds me of a poem." Much of my education and life views were shaped around our family dinner table, where we talked about literature and politics and current life.

When I graduated from high school at age seventeen, I started a diary. The first entry expresses the view that has sustained me throughout my life:

> I have just graduated from High School. I have an attitude towards life that I would like to preserve forever. I should like on these pages to make this attitude very tangible so that if I should ever forget—if I should ever live without a sense of beauty, idealism, love, and happiness—I will be able to refer to these pages and remember once again.
>
> I ask myself at seventeen
> Am I happy?
> And I answer
> Yes!
> I am quite complete for seventeen.
>
> I ask myself at seventeen
> Will I be happier at seventy

When my face is wrinkled and my body grows stiff?
And I answer
Yes!
I hope to be more complete at seventy.

I ask myself at seventeen
Shall I wait and store up all my happiness
For that day when my body grows stiff
And I have achieved my full completeness?
And I answer
No!

I shall live each day and each moment
As the most beautiful day I can expect.
And yet, in my youth—in my eagerness—in my heart
I know that each moment in store for me
Holds greater depth and greater beauty.

THIS IS A MOMENT!

Despite my wholesome family environment, I was relatively shy, and I never felt that I lived up to my parents' view of me. When I received an *A* on a high school paper, I always thought that if my mother hadn't corrected the spelling of two words, I would not have gotten that *A*. In my freshman year at Cornell, during the first week in English 101, we had to read a brief page and write a short paragraph commenting on what it meant to us. I was up all night, working on my answer until sunrise, wondering how I would make it through college. Any confidence I felt came not from my own conviction but from the praise of others.

In my graduating yearbook from Brooklyn's Midwood High School, one of my teachers wrote, "I shall never forget your award presentation to Eleanor Roosevelt. It was as moving and powerful as the Gettysburg Address." I remember that day well. Eleanor Roosevelt had been invited to receive our school's FDR Memorial

Award for Brotherhood and Tolerance, and I was chosen to make the presentation remarks. Afterwards, Mrs. Roosevelt told the principal, "I am taking her with me to the UN for the day." We rode together in her limousine, talking all the way from Brooklyn to the United Nations about life and goals and dreams.

Experiences like these began to give me more confidence. Eventually, inspired by the values I learned as a young woman, I began to take on leadership roles in local community and national organizations. I never sought any of the positions I held. Each time one was offered, I debated whether to accept. By the end of my twenties, an inner voice told me, "We are what we do—not what we think we can do." Ady encouraged me to accept these positions and was exceedingly proud. Many of these roles involved writing and public speaking. I believe the urge, throughout my adult life, to communicate what was of vital importance to me, and in later years to help others cope with the multiple challenges that Alzheimer's imposes, led to this book.

In every capacity, no matter how great the responsibility, what I received back was tenfold what I may have given. My life has been enriched by beautiful friendships with people I would never have known. I have helped to encourage countless young women to take on roles of responsibility. I have lived with a sense of meaning and purpose. Ultimately these experiences would provide a crucial underpinning to my role as a caregiver.

Our Lives Together

Ady and I married in June, almost ten months after we met, between my junior and senior years in college. We lived in Riverdale, New York, until I graduated from Barnard. Then, at Ady's father's urging, we moved down to join Ady's parents in Florida, followed, about six months later, by his sister and her husband, Binky and Lenny Miller. After spending about a year and a half looking for appropriate work and depleting whatever savings we had, we finally found an unusual building venture. Neither Ady nor Lenny knew anything about building, but with the help of Ady's father, they went into partnership with an established builder in South Florida and built six low-priced houses. Ady's father provided the money and the builder provided the know-how. Any profits were to be split fifty-fifty.

It was an intense learning experience. By the time those six houses were completed, Ady and Lenny knew a lot about building. The young men offered to continue the partnership on an equal financial basis, but the established builder wished them luck and said they were ready to proceed without him. In 1959 they established Pasadena Homes. Ady became president of the company. "The boys," as they were affectionately known by both customers and sub-contractors, purchased sixty-one lots and offered four

Wedding of Helene and Ady

models to choose from. Economic times were not good. When they put the work out to bid, plumbers, electricians, carpenters, and other professionals lined up around the block seeking employment. Most of the subcontractors they chose stayed with Pasadena Homes for decades. The boys worried they were overpriced for the market: their two- and three-bedroom models, with an abundance of custom choices, were priced from $12,300 to $15,750, while the homes of the builder across the street started at $8,750. They put a full-page ad in the Miami *Herald.* Hundreds of interested buyers showed up. As the actual construction proceeded, Ady, with his engineering degree from Dartmouth, handled most of the preliminary construction, taking constant notes, counting every nail, and calculating every cubic yard of concrete. After the basic construction stage, Lenny took over. He was great at making people feel at home, helping customers select interiors, colors, and features for the outside of the home. It was a natural division of the work.

Though Ady and I would go on to have different careers, early in our marriage we learned to work together with mutual respect. Pasadena Homes had no realtors, no sales staff. The family was put to work, and we became sales people overnight. Our full sales staff consisted of Ady and Lenny; Ady's parents, Sadie and Joe; Aunt Rosie and Uncle Freddie; Ady's sister, Binky; and me. Ady and Lenny gave us a crash course on what was unique about a Pasadena Home. For example, the gables of almost all homes built in Florida at the time had wood trusses. Pasadena Homes, at Ady's insistence, used solid poured concrete gables. In a hurricane-prone area, this was an important feature. Years later, wood trusses would no longer pass Florida code.

The potential buyers liked the quality they saw, the setting surrounded by lakes, the numerous choices that were offered, and the integrity they sensed. We never needed to place another ad: the sales were all word of mouth. Once a contract was concluded, it

Ady mid-career

seemed as if each buyer encouraged everyone they knew to follow them. Very soon there was a huge waitlist.

I still recall the thrill of selling the first Pasadena Home. I was a young mother with a two-year-old son, whom I left at home with a sitter. I had never done anything like this before, and I was more than a little nervous. I can still see one of the early couples that came. They had two spectacularly beautiful daughters, ages about ten and twelve, each with thick blond braids down to their waists. I blurted out, "Your daughters look like they stepped out of a Thomas Mann novel!" I immediately berated myself for being so inappropriate. Given the relatively low price range of the homes, I had no idea what education level to expect in potential buyers. But the father responded with a huge smile. "We think so, too!" He was an English teacher. His wife and the girls studied every inch of the models while the husband and I discussed literature. About an hour later, the wife and daughters returned, smiling. The wife said, "We love the homes. We're ready to sign a contract now and get the choice pick of the lots on the water." The memory of being the "sales person" for the first Pasadena Home and helping to launch my husband's business is one I still treasure.

The company's continuing reputation for integrity, fairness, quality, and deep caring for their customers lasted throughout Ady and Lenny's forty-five years of building.

Ady and I had two children and four grandchildren, two from each child. Our son, Mark, became a cardiologist. As Ady and I grew older, we turned to Mark not only for medical advice but for guidance on just about everything in life. To this day, I do not make any important decision without running it by him. Our daughter, Bonnie, inherited her father's love of mathematical reasoning and became a tenured professor of mathematics at MIT. She has received numerous awards and is called upon to speak around the world. Though Mark and Bonnie did not live near us, they provided constant and crucial love, support, and guidance throughout Ady's Alzheimer's years.

At Ady's 75th birthday party, a friend toasting him said, "No one ever had a bad word to say about Ady Berger." People who knew

Ady and family

Ady would describe him as a bright and ethical man. Yet despite his financial success, he was humble, kind, and gentle and never adopted that self-assured swagger that so many successful men acquire. He remained a quiet and simple guy who loved his wife and family with unfaltering devotion and enjoyed music and math, swimming, and biking. After he passed away I received almost five hundred long letters—not just the typical "I'm sorry for your loss" but heartfelt words about what Ady meant to them personally. As our last years together progressed and I watched him handle the changes in his life with such grace, I understood how blessed I was to be married to Ady Berger.

That is why, years ago, before I had the remotest idea of how to deal with the decline unfolding before me, a whisper of a voice within me said, "Remember who this kind, gentle, and loving man was, and give him the respect and dignity he earned throughout his life."

Challenges

Ady had his faults, as everyone does, and even the most loving relationships have many challenging moments. My relationship with Ady's parents was difficult for many years. I was not the bride they had selected for their son. When we returned from our honeymoon, his parents informed us that we were moving to Mexico for Ady to run a paper business that one of his father's friends was starting. Ady's commitment to my parents when he asked for my hand in marriage was that I would complete my senior year at Barnard College. After a disastrous meeting with both sets of parents, we chose not to go. My relationship with Ady's parents was virtually over for about thirty years. They rarely saw our children, even though we lived in the same town and continued to make overtures. To be rejected by one's parents would be hard for anyone, but especially for a man as sensitive as Ady.

We had our share of difficult times in the early years. The relationship with his parents was very hard on both of us and had a clear negative impact on our marriage. We were two very different people and went through lots of therapy and growing pains. What each of us had going for us was the conviction that the other was worth the struggle of working things out.

. . .

Eight months after our son, Mark, was born, when I was 22, my mother died. She was 52. A year earlier she had had brain surgery. It was initially pronounced successful, but a week later she had a stroke caused by a blood clot in the brain and lost the ability to speak. The loss at that early age was overwhelming for me. I had turned to her for guidance on every decision, large or small. My mother was open and direct with me, never with a hidden agenda. I didn't always appreciate that as a child, as she often issued advice on matters I probably could have figured out myself. Yet I always knew that her guidance was wise and, as I grew older, that she had an abundance of faith in me and my judgement. Now she was gone.

Fortunately, my father was introduced to a wonderful woman whom he married within a year. I became very close to her, as she had never had a child. She enriched my father's life for seventeen good years and then devotedly cared for him for another ten years after he had a stroke—but more about her role later.

Despite losing my mother at such a young age, I managed to grow up with optimism and a positive attitude toward life. Perhaps that stemmed from the love and encouragement that my parents surrounded me with as a child. My childhood optimism became a lifelong view that helped to sustain me through the difficult periods that were still to come.

. . .

The greatest challenges Ady and I faced together were the many surgeries, some very serious, that Ady endured, often with prolonged discomfort and anxiety beforehand and long recovery periods. He had weak lungs, a condition dating back to a deadly form of pneumonia he contracted in the Air Force. Many months of antibiotics kept him alive but left permanent abscesses on his lungs.

By 1966, when Ady was thirty-seven years old, he was so short of breath that he was unable to walk across a room. Doctors recommended a lobectomy—surgery to remove an infected lobe in his lung—as the only course. After the surgery, he was incapacitated for months; he suffered for the rest of his life from chronic bronchiectasis. The repeated pneumonias that followed over the years often required intravenous antibiotics, administered with a line that remained in his vein for weeks.

In 1988, Ady was hit by a bus while riding his bike, which required hip surgery. A week after the surgery, he developed a life-threatening blood clot in the groin and spent another three weeks in the hospital, the first half confined entirely to his bed to prevent the clot from traveling to the heart.

He had two prostate surgeries: a minor procedure in 1988 and a major surgery in 1991. After being diagnosed with prostate cancer, he reviewed the options and chose to undergo the difficult radical prostatectomy. It turned out to be a wise choice because his death seventeen years later had nothing to do with cancer.

In 1999 he had angioplasty, with a stent inserted into the circumflex artery to restore blood flow to his heart.

In 2000 he had two operations, knee surgery and a hernia repair.

In 2005, when another severe pneumonia caused a life-threatening pulmonary embolism, a filter was inserted in his lung.

In 2009, during the Alzheimer's years, after a fall in the bathroom, he needed another partial hip replacement (in the opposite hip that was fractured 20 years before).

As I write this, I wonder how Ady managed to find joy and contentment despite this long list (which omits his lifelong asthma and many less dramatic medical issues). In looking back, perhaps I should have known that he would find peace even amidst the grave challenges of Alzheimer's.

. . .

Whatever success Ady and I achieved together arose from hard work and a commitment to the marriage and to each other. Throughout our long years together, we encountered many problems. Every marriage has its ups and downs, and ours was certainly not all smooth sailing. But our commitment to each other was solid and not only survived the storms but came through intact and strong. If anything, the hardships we weathered together made us better able to conquer the challenges of the Alzheimer's years.

CHAPTER FOUR

Background & Early Stages

Worrisome Signs

THROUGHOUT OUR YEARS OF MARRIAGE, UNTIL THE mental slippage began, Ady was the most responsible person I had ever met. If I asked for his help and he agreed, I literally checked it off my list as complete. So my discomfort was huge when atypical behavior became repetitive.

At first the behavior seemed merely incidental. We were checking out of a hotel after a wedding. I went to empty the safe deposit box, asking Ady to check out. In the taxi leaving the hotel I asked, "Honey, you checked out?"

"No, I forgot. Let's go back."

His desk at home was typically piled high with documents or floor plans he was working on. But gradually I realized that some of the papers there had become obsolete several years before. We began to have arguments when he refused to part with anything. It was almost as if throwing the paper out would be parting with the memory of it.

He not only misplaced things more often than usual but developed a paranoid suspicion that someone took them. I recall my alarm when, on a cruise in the late 1990s, Ady said angrily, "Someone took my pajama top!" I opened my eyes wide and took a sad inward breadth, trying to hide my dismay, when I saw that he was wearing it. He had put it over his shirt because he was chilly. I'm happy to recall that, instinctively, I responded not with a negative scolding tone implying, "What's wrong with you? You're wearing it!" but rather with a pat on his cheek and a smile. "Sweetie, you're wearing it." We both laughed. But inside I knew the dreaded significance.

Many of us are somewhat discombobulated in strange or new settings, but Ady's behavior was becoming too unlike him to ignore. On the same cruise, he woke one morning and said, "Someone stole my medicine." It was exactly where he kept it, in his night table drawer. He had just forgotten where. I was more worried about Ady's belief that it was stolen than about his forgetting where it was.

Fiftieth anniversary, several months before diagnosis

Of course, we all go through lapses, forgetting names, not recognizing faces, not remembering where we met friends or what their profession is. None of these in themselves are unusual, but when they become repetitive, we know we can't dismiss our concerns.

Early Stages and Testing

In today's climate of almost daily advances in medical science and with the encouraging results of new medications, there is the hope that early detection may have a positive impact—if not yet in preventing, at least in postponing symptoms. New drugs, if taken early enough, alone or in combination with other medications, may slow cognitive decline. It is important to investigate all the options with your doctor. Some of the medications may have minimal improvement and are not free of side effects. Proper evaluation by a doctor who is familiar with the latest research on Alzheimer's is crucial.

A diagnosis of Alzheimer's is rarely a surprise, as the troubling signs have undoubtedly already begun to mount. Yet the medical diagnosis of what you have observed is essential.

Most of Ady's doctors throughout his life were outstanding. They were there for us with both knowledge and compassion. Our experiences with those who administered and reported on the psychological testing, however, were far less satisfactory. They did not know Ady or factor in his exceedingly high IQ scores; they referred only to the norms of the average population. On these scales, even with Ady's great impairment, he still fell in the "normal" range, and he scored well above the standard norms on those early psychological tests. Alarm bells did not go off.

In fact, these reports consistently editorialized that each of us was overreacting because of Ady's parents' history with Alzheimer's. One early report actually stated, "The wife is overly concerned because both his mother and father had Alzheimer's." I believe that today I would have reacted differently to this put-down of a woman's observations of her husband. Perhaps the relief I felt with "normal results" lured me into shortchanging my instincts and ignoring what I knew.

I was stunned to realize, as I went through our old records, that it took *twenty-four years* from Ady's first neuropsychological evaluation in 1981 until we received the definitive diagnosis in 2005.

In the early years, although I never consciously thought, "There's potentially a real problem here," I observed the signs I just described and took action to explore further. Ady was cooperative and did not object to being tested. I believe he was aware of the changes that were taking place and was somewhat relieved that we were taking action. We repeated the same testing two and five years later, in 1983 and 1986.

The results of this large battery of tests were fascinating in their inconsistency. While most of his scores were above average, in the "very superior range of intellectual functioning," others were way below expectation for a person of Ady's IQ. The 1981 report states, "A pattern such as this is thought to be reflective of a regression from a previously higher level of functioning." But the testing was inconclusive: he was still in the above-normal range, and no action was recommended.

In May of 2000, an MRI of Ady's brain "showed mild to moderate diffuse brain atrophy." One neurologist did suggest Aricept, which is used to treat mild to moderate dementia caused by Alzheimer's disease. Ady unfortunately rejected it after a few days, claiming that he did not like the way it made him feel. I may have suggested that he begin with half a pill until he got used to it, but I did not insist. I'll never know if it would have slowed the progression if I had.

The testing was repeated March 25, 2002, three years before the official diagnosis of Alzheimer's, by a clinical neuropsychologist. The results were reminiscent of the earlier reports:

> The results of the present reevaluation do not indicate any significant cognitive decline from the patient's previous evaluation approximately two years before. In fact, some of the scores were substantially higher. This gentleman has outstanding verbal capacities with his immediate and delayed verbal memory being average and his nonverbal/visual memory being mildly impaired. There is no evidence of any type of cerebral dysfunction and specifically no evidence of any progressive decline. The question to be addressed is: why does the patient, as well as his wife, report that they feel that his memory is getting worse. Several factors might account for this. One is that the patient, if put in a situation where he is pressed for time, probably did not attend or concentrate. As mentioned previously, he needs time to process information. Consequently, he is likely to be more forgetful [he was only in the fourteenth percentile on a measure of delayed visual memory]. However, if he verbally mediated tasks to be remembered [in other words, if Ady said them aloud to himself], he should remember them well.

Once again, a different reading of the psychological testing dismissed the report of both husband and wife:

> I also believe that, considering the fact that both of his parents were diagnosed with Alzheimer's disease, both he and his wife are more apprehensive of the condition and probably make more out of memory lapses than the test data would indicate. *The patient is not in need of any neuropsychological follow-up at the present time* [emphasis mine].

How could the tester state that "the patient is not in need of any neuropsychological follow-up at the present time" with the vast discrepancy between highs that were off the charts and lows in the fourteenth percentile? I believe that a wife's (or husband's) observations should not be discarded—especially when the patient expresses his own misgivings about loss of both memory and daily functioning. A person knows his or her own mind. And *you* know your loved one better than any practitioner who performs neurological tests for a few hours and knows nothing about the person your loved one was. I saw the decline, I knew it was beyond normal aging, and yet I foolishly accepted the neurological reports based on "normal" tests results. Perhaps I should have pursued my observations more rigorously. Perhaps earlier treatment might have slowed the progression of Ady's impairment. I'll never know the answer.

This might be a good time to suggest that as caregivers, no matter how much effort we expend, we sometimes tend to beat ourselves up for not doing more, for not having the foresight or hindsight to understand what at the time was inexplicable to us. "Woulda, coulda, shoulda" are not constructive thoughts. We are all human and doing the best we can in a situation none of us wants to be in.

Misgivings, Denial—and Action

It is puzzling for me to comprehend the dichotomy in my mind before the official diagnosis. On the one hand, I never consciously acknowledged that a potential major problem was looming. On the other hand, it was clear that Ady was starting to need more help, and I took action accordingly. Here are two clear examples of this dichotomy—simultaneous denial and action:

Our family knew a wonderful, reliable, and capable woman, Mary Hempfling. She initially worked for Ady's father, but for twenty years had been coming to our home two Sundays a month to help with paperwork and paying monthly bills. About two years *before* the definitive diagnosis, I asked Mary if she would be willing to come in three days a week so that Ady could teach her all his complicated record keeping and financial management systems—while he was still able.

Still in the midst of another job, Mary was initially hesitant and asked if she could wait for one year. My response was, "A year may be too late." Mary agreed and in the ensuing years freed me to concentrate my attentions on Ady and relieved me of many essential responsibilities. To this day, I depend deeply on Mary's wisdom, thoroughness, and friendship.

In November of 2003, I was elected National Chair of the Jewish Education Service of North America (JESNA). The election to that office was for a year's term, but by tradition the chair usually served for three years. I loved my role, but it took a lot of energy, time, and travel to JESNA's central office in New York. In the first months of my second term, more than a year before Dr. Duara pronounced "Alzheimer's," I told the executive director of JESNA that mine would have to be a two-year term. I expressed my concerns about Ady, explaining that I anticipated his needing more care.

I still find it difficult to believe that I could have taken these concrete and often difficult steps without openly admitting to myself the severity of Ady's decline. I guess that's what we call *denial.* It is so easy to be in denial because we so deeply fear knowing the reality. We fervently hope that the signs we observe are no more than just typical aging. There are countless telling moments that by themselves are typical of all of us and so easy to excuse—until they start to add up, and one morning you wake up and understand that they cannot be ignored any longer.

Ironically, my path to facing the issue head-on was through a side door, well before our appointment at the Wein Center for Memory Disorder. For decades, Ady's greatest medical problems had been pulmonary. As those issues were becoming more complex, our son advised us to go to National Jewish Health (NJH), an academic medical research facility located in Denver, Colorado, which specialized in respiratory disorders. Their diagnostic plan is unique. The patient comes for a week to ten days as an outpatient. Only very ill patients remain in the hospital; most stay in a nearby hotel, report to the hospital at 8 A.M., and remain there until 5 or 6 P.M. Each patient is assigned their own hospital room as a base to meet with doctors, leave their personal items, or take a rest during the day. Typically they assign each patient a lead physician in addition to a team of many physicians with different specialties, who perform multiple tests and meet to evaluate the patient's condition. Ady and I were there for ten days.

At the conclusion of the tests, they completely changed Ady's respiratory protocol. Ady was an excellent patient and followed their complex instructions exactly for the rest of his life, which gave him years of comfortable breathing. At the final evaluation meeting, the doctors recommended, in addition to solutions for the respiratory issues we came in for, immediate consultation with a neurologist. They explained that Ady had severe issues with either dementia or incipient Alzheimer's, as evidenced by their numerous tests and his increasing symptoms. Their CAT scan showed evidence of possible hydrocephalus, brain atrophy, and/or frontotemporal dementia.

With that recommendation from NJH, Ady's symptoms—the continuing decrease of memory and abilities, getting lost while driving to familiar places, inappropriate behavior—could no longer be ignored. I sought the help of a well-recommended psychiatrist. Little did I know what an outstanding choice Dr. Ellen Rees would be. Her wisdom became an essential guide to me throughout the last six years of Ady's life and has continued to keep me whole during the years since his passing. (This book would not have become a reality without Dr. Rees's encouragement and urging, letting me know that I had something of real value to impart.) After her initial meetings with us both, Dr. Rees said, "I don't know what I'm dealing with here. I don't know whether this is psychological or physical." She recommended that we have Ady tested locally, focusing on the neurological issues. It was a relief for me to know that I was being guided by a knowledgeable, interested person rather than handling all the decisions on my own. I understood early on that I had no experience with what was unfolding and found it extremely helpful and comforting to bring someone on board to advise me. It allowed me to sleep at night without wondering what I had neglected to do.

By the end of the summer of 2005, when Ady was seventy-five years old, the neurological evaluation confirmed what we were told at NJH, adding "childish and inappropriate behavior, and executive dysfunction" to the previous report.

Testing and Official Diagnosis

I had my marching orders and plunged in. The range of opinions from the different doctors was confusing. In October of 2005, however, we were fortunate to get an appointment with Dr. Ranjan Duara, the brilliant, devoted, and caring director of the state-of-the-art Wien Center for Memory Disorder in Miami Beach. Ady spent many hours being tested. We then met in Dr. Duara's office for the fateful diagnosis. The word "Alzheimer's" was certainly not a shock, but it was devastating nonetheless. Dr. Duara would prove to be the guardian angel who guided us through the difficult years ahead with kindness, warmth, intelligence, and encouragement. Yet despite Dr. Duara's care, the prospect of what lay ahead was hard for Ady and me to accept.

Need for Patient and Family to Be Informed

I was stunned to read, four years after Ady's passing, a *Wall Street Journal* article headlined, "Doctors Don't Say It's Alzheimer's."* The article begins, "More than half of people with Alzheimer's

* *Wall Street Journal,* March 24, 2015

disease have never been told by their doctors that they have the condition, according to a new study from the Alzheimer's Association. This means that people are being robbed of the opportunity to make important decisions about their lives." The article goes on: "90% of patients with cardiovascular disease or breast or prostate cancer were told of their conditions," while "of the patients whose doctors listed an Alzheimer's diagnosis in their Medicare claims, only 45% said in the surveys that they'd been told they had the disease."

Ady and I were fortunate to have doctors throughout who were completely open, kind, and professional with each of us. We never experienced this kind of deception or withholding of information—but I was appalled by these statistics. Keeping both patients and caregivers in the dark is to me a cowardly and unethical breach of trust and responsibility. I cannot fathom a doctor assuming the right to make the decision as to whether the patient or family is informed. Every patient must be given the opportunity to prepare appropriate documents like wills, health care proxies, power of attorney, and so on, and to plan for their lives and that of their family, for example by moving from a home to an apartment while they still have the capacity to do so. Every family member must be given the opportunity to understand what's happening, so they can react with compassion rather than anger when the behavior of their loved one changes.

Again, every one of the doctors who treated Ady was totally above board with us, but I would urge anyone who suspects a problem to demand answers and, if they are not forthcoming, to change physicians.

After the Definitive Diagnosis

After all the conflicting early reports, I can't say it was a relief, but it was somewhat settling to have a definitive diagnosis. I had not the remotest notion of how to deal with the problem, but at least it was defined. The beginning was far from easy. Ady started down the predicted path: still depressed, still not accepting the new reality, still argumentative. At every doctor's appointment, the doctor or nurse would take me in the hallway and let me know what I was in for. Their warnings included anger, impatience, temper, depression, and even violence. In the next few months, all their predictions except the violence began to be realized.

My learning began. How do I give him the best life possible? How do I bolster myself and deal with the overwhelming sadness within me? I kept reminding myself daily how blessed my life had been. All our lives are determined by the myriads of decisions we make every day, some minor, some major. How we frame a situation in our own minds clearly affects our attitude. I was in new territory, with a fierce commitment to learn what would make our journey easier. I learned from my mistakes as well as from observing what worked. I learned from intently watching Ady's reactions—whether positive or negative. I learned from both seeking guidance from others and observing others. I knew I did not have the answers and greeted each dilemma like a sponge, soaking up all that I could.

What I could not have imagined during those early days and months was the unanticipated and remarkable success story that would unfold, success measured both by Ady's vast improvement in memory and function and by this becoming a happy and growing time for each of us. The warnings the doctors and nurses issued were given with kindness and were intended to help, to prepare me. As it turned out, they were a far greater help than they could have envisioned, as I'll explain in the next chapter.

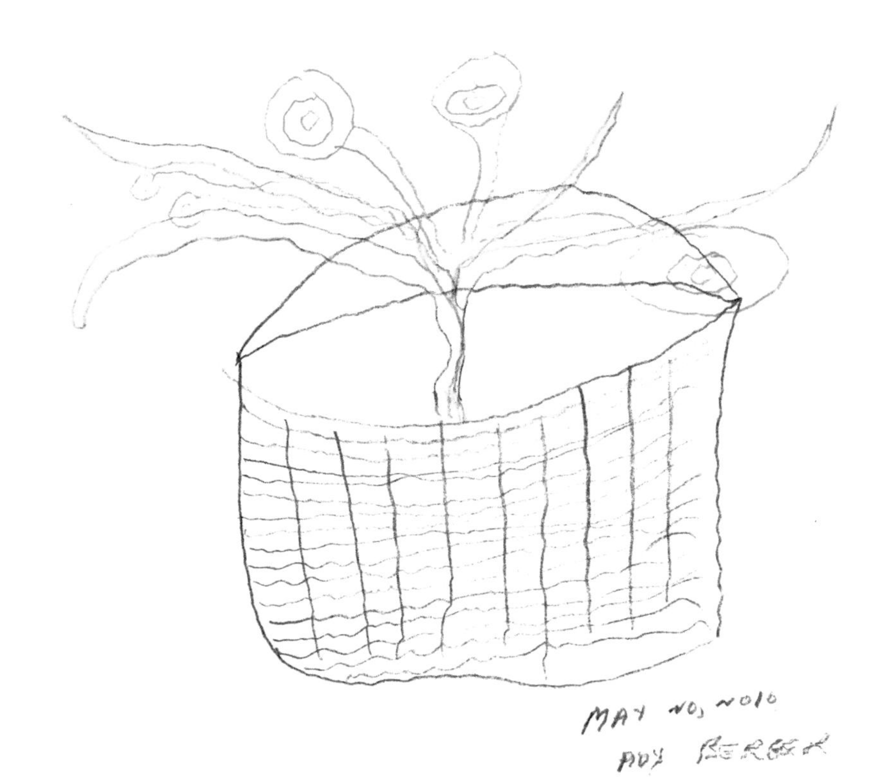
MAY 20, 2010
ROY BERGER

PART TWO

PRACTICAL APPROACHES

The whole value of doing good lies in the loving kindness that inspires it.

—TALMUD: SUKKAH 49B

PART TWO IS THE ROAD MAP FOR THE CONCRETE METHODS that worked for Ady and me and those who helped care for him. It is what I learned through trial and error, along with what I learned from others, sometimes in the form of advice, often through observation of both positive and negative behavior in others or myself.

I'd like to define what I mean when I say "what worked for us." The next six years turned into a happy, creative, loving time, with what eventually became a shocking but indisputable improvement in Ady's memory and functioning. He went from staring at a light bulb during most of a dinner with friends, to being engaged and focused and asking questions about their lives (even if he did not remember the answers the next day). He returned to playing the piano about an hour each day, after two or three years of abandoning it. He learned new games like Sudoku—which, when introduced in the early stages, was incomprehensible to him. Finally, as I have related, on the night before he died, of unrelated causes, Ady greeted each of the seventeen guests at the dinner table by name.

These and many other changes were totally unexpected. Despite the sadness of watching the man Ady once was diminish, it was exhilarating to see his consistent progress, to hear his daily expressions of love and appreciation, and to be surrounded by his ever-present smile. In the years since he's been gone, I still hear constantly from close friends and those who knew him only from a distance, how they remember his sweetness and his smile.

CHAPTER FIVE

Acceptance

YOU'VE RECEIVED THE OFFICIAL DIAGNOSIS. FOR MOST of us it's not a surprise. We took our loved one for testing because we were concerned that this would be the verdict. But the confirmation of the diagnosis we feared does not automatically lead to acceptance. That takes work to achieve. Until there is acceptance, it is difficult to take the steps that must be taken, or to fully plan what's best for your loved one's life and for your own.

I did not recognize, when we received Ady's diagnosis, how vastly my own life was about to change. Nor did I take stock of what abilities I might utilize to keep our lives as comfortable as possible. I certainly did not comprehend that I didn't have to passively watch his decline. Had I realized that I could influence or change Ady's situation, I might have avoided some of those awful feelings of being trapped. The more you are able to accept that your own life will never be the same, the better you will be able to deal with the challenges ahead.

Acceptance takes not only work but time. The reality is that you've likely started caregiving already. The daily demands are not going to go away. The sooner you accept this new, harsh reality, the more energy you'll have, and the more focus you will be able to direct to the strategic planning that will be required.

Learning from Everybody

The rabbis say: "Who is wise? One who learns from every person."* The following short vignettes illustrate how we can begin to function in a responsible way only when we come to terms with reality.

Life Goes On

When I looked back, wondering if I had the strength for the level of acceptance I would need to cope with the difficulties that lay ahead, I thought back to the time decades earlier when I got the call from my dad that my mother had died. The news was expected but still devastating. My beautiful, accomplished mother was fifty-two. I was twenty-two. When Dad's call came in, I was giving breakfast to our first child, who was eight months old. I remember so vividly wanting to cry, wanting to react, wanting to crumble. But I had a child to feed. This was not the time to fall apart. I pulled myself together, knowing that I had plenty of time to grieve and mourn later, and fed our child. This was not the moment for an emotional meltdown. It was, instead, an immediate and powerful lesson: I had just lost my mother. I needed to feed my son. Accept both realities. Life goes on.

The Soothing Finality of Facts

Ady and I were on a plane headed home to Miami. A man and his wife were seated in the aisle directly across from us. The man was trying to get his daughter, originally on a New York flight that had

---

* *Wisdom of the Fathers,* 4:1

just been canceled, a ticket on the Miami flight. Our section was pretty empty while the rest of the plane was filling up. The man was like a wild animal in a rage: he saw nothing but empty seats, but the stewardess kept telling him that the flight was full. As his anger escalated, I sat quietly watching the scene unfold. Slowly, the seats around us filled up. All were occupied. Once the man accepted that nothing more could be done, he became a docile passenger on the plane, reading a book the entire flight and behaving like a perfect gentleman.

It was an important teaching experience for me, offered unconsciously by a total stranger: When we cannot change the facts, we experience useless anger until we accept them—and a sense of calm when we do.

A Friend's Guidance That Helped to Sustain Me

In the early years of Ady's incipient Alzheimer's, before the official diagnosis, I remember a conversation that helped to shape how I dealt with the reality that was daily looming more heavily on me. At the time I had probably expressed my concerns about Ady to none but my closest friends. We were out to dinner with a lovely couple whom we knew quite well. Dr. Samuel Berkowitz was a clinical professor of pediatric dentistry and surgery, a widely published author and authority. Although we had known this for years, Ady, sitting next to him, turned and said, "So, Sam, what do you do?"

I blanched and tried to come to Ady's rescue, rushing in to remind Ady of Sam's prestigious accomplishments. His wife, Lynn, took my hand and said, "Helene, everybody loves Ady for Ady. Don't try to cover for him."

My eyes filled with tears realizing how obvious Ady's deterioration was. Though the Alzheimer's diagnosis was not yet clear, the nature of Ady's condition was hard enough. Trying to keep secret what had become clear to others only made it more difficult. Lynn's guidance was my first step toward open, public acceptance of our new reality. It was easier after that for me to acknowledge our problem openly, to shed the burden of pretending that everything was normal.

Publically acknowledging what Ady and I were experiencing, rather than treating it as embarrassing and shameful, gave me enormous relief. It opened up new worlds of communication for me, enabling me to learn from others' experience. Ady himself made it easier, as he began to admit openly that, "My memory's not so good anymore." Though our reluctance to openly acknowledge our new reality was understandable, it burdened us with an unnecessary level of sadness and pain. Just as important, we lost out on the wise counsel and compassion that friends can offer. In two six-word sentences, Lynn's honesty and compassion changed my life. I will always be grateful to her.

Coming to Terms with the Patient's Capabilities

The struggle to accept a "dread decree" like Alzheimer's, dementia, or life with chronic pain can often last for years. Every degree of decline on the part of our spouse or loved one is a new punch in the gut. We still want and expect the old behavior, and debilitating anger begins to seep in. I found that my own acceptance varied from issue to issue. Some problems were easier to accept, while others put me into a tailspin.

For example, though I was able to accept Ady's loss of memory quite early—probably because I had been living with it for many years—it took me much longer to accept that this brilliant, mathematically inclined man could no longer manage his time or had difficulty with simple arithmetic. Ady used to refer to himself as a "numbers man" because of his love of and ability with numbers.

Now he would insist that he'd be on time for his physical therapist when he had thirty-odd minutes to go before the appointment—but an hour and fifteen minutes of medical treatments to finish before she arrived. My own frustration and anger would often flair. "You're a mathematician! How do you imagine that you can do 75 minutes of treatments in 33 minutes?" And on it would go. I could not accept it. What was worse, when I expressed my annoyance, Ady would look at me like a wounded puppy. That deeply hurt look, knowing that he had disappointed me, was like an arrow plunging into my heart. I had to come to terms with the reality that no matter how he may have functioned earlier in his life, that was then, and this was now. He was simply no longer capable of planning his own time. My expectations had to change.

The Power of Data

While I spoke earlier about some limitations of psychological testing, the testing that followed, a brain scan by Dr. Duara, was one that changed my life. Dr. Duara pointed out on the scan large areas of black empty spaces where brain tissue should have been. When Dr. Duara looked at that MRI with me he said, "If I had seen this scan before speaking with Ady and seeing his excellent test results, I never would have believed that anyone with this much damage could do as well as he did. He wants to. He just can't."

With those words, I got it. The results of the brain scan I viewed evoked both my complete compassion and the ability to move on. I left Dr. Duara's office with an overwhelming, indescribable sadness and overwhelming, indescribable relief. The fight was over. Witnessing the brain scan results freed me to appreciate the man that Ady still was. My role was to give this precious, sweet, loving man the love and support he needed and deserved. It was humbling to know that despite my managerial skills and commitment, despite the ideal atmosphere that I tried to create with determination, with energy, with incalculable time, I now understood that I was not that powerful.

The Patient's Own Acceptance

To make life easier for everyone, we try to encourage the patient's own acceptance. That, I'm afraid, is the most difficult to achieve. But I believe that, even here, your own attitude can make a difference. If you treat your new role with frustration and annoyance at every diminution, that anger will spread to your patient like a virus. The more you can muster up support and kindness, remembering always that he or she did not choose this condition either, the more likely it is for your loved one to understand that you are there for the long haul and that he will not be abandoned.

Once Ady got over his initial depression and understood that I was there for him 100 percent, he began to accept his changing condition with more grace than I thought was humanly possible. His positive attitude, in turn, affected me profoundly. In the beginning, part of whatever gentleness, kindness, and patience I could bring forth stemmed from seeing that my supportive attitude worked wonders and made my own life easier. Within a short time, my own behavior stemmed from my total respect and admiration for Ady's dignity and acceptance of his condition. I can honestly say that after more than fifty years of marriage, my love for and appreciation of my husband not only did not diminish, they grew. The love he felt from me was completely authentic, and he thrived on it. Knowing that I had a lot to do with his radiant smile made me happy. Virtually every night, after his good-night kiss, he still expressed with varying words, "I love you so much, and I appreciate all that you are doing for me." He expressed his own appreciation and love for me verbally and in writing—and I, in turn, thrived on that. After the first year I stopped thinking "poor me" and began thinking "lucky me" to be married to such a man.

I understand how fortunate I was with the outcome we had. I certainly understand that every Alzheimer's patient will not react as Ady did. Yet I strongly believe that the more one can create a loving atmosphere, the more one can soften or avoid any expression of disappointment or impatience, the more likely the patient is to thrive. I found that my tone with Ady was even more important than the words. The more he felt respected, accepted, and loved, the less likely he was to have a hostile reaction. Soon any trace of hostility vanished. This is the same principle we apply to good parenting. To help keep a child happy and not rebellious, we surround him with security, with respect, with genuine praise for what he does well, with consistency, with acceptance, with honesty, and with love.

As expressed throughout this chapter, acceptance is not easy. It comes slowly. Each person discovers his or her own way to find it. If you are fortunate enough to make peace with the circumstances you are in, you can use that energy, instead of fighting your fate, to become creative in building a supportive world for your loved one. We may not be able to change the reality we are faced with, but we do have control over the perspective we choose to bring to it.

Separation and Guilt

In the beginning, I became aware that I needed to separate myself slightly, or the pain was too great. That subtle pulling away gave me the perspective to cope. However, when I realized that my initial instinctive behavior was partially for my benefit, my emotions were compounded with guilt, even though that slight pulling back was only for a very brief period.

I record this harsh self-judgement because I think that at some point, all of us as caregivers add a feeling of guilt to our other burdens. No matter how hard we try, there are days when we're sure we're not doing enough. I think it's important to recognize that those questions and feelings, though understandable, are not productive. Whatever we do to keep ourselves functioning, whole, and sane is necessary. We are often more generous about the failings of our loved one than we are about our own. We need to give ourselves permission to be human.

What *Not* to Accept

Because of the repeated warnings about what was ahead of me, I was terrified with each unwanted behavior that emerged during the first year. I vowed to do everything in my power to postpone the negative conduct. When I found myself thinking, "That's not so bad. I can live with that," some inner voice screamed, *No, you can't!*—no more than you would allow a toddler to get away with unacceptable behavior, knowing that bad habits form rapidly and are difficult to reverse. I pounced like a tiger, not even letting a cross look go by without letting Ady know how that look affected me. That may sound harsh, but it was expressed in the most loving way, often while patting his cheek and beginning with words like, "Dear, do you know how much I love you?" Then I would explain how that look was hurtful to me. When engaged in a real conversation, he almost always ended up feeling closer to me and thanking me for being honest and open. "Honey, please keep telling me," he would say. "I love you too much to hurt you."

The Family's Reaction

Throughout this chapter, I've discussed the need for acceptance by both the caregiver and the patient. It is equally important to guide your family (and even other caregivers who might be assisting you) to accept the changes they are about to experience. No one is ever ready to see the person they love diminished. If your family is not responding in a way that offers compassion and support, it may take more than one conversation on your part to help them understand that this debilitating condition is not one that their loved one has chosen. You might encourage them to remember the good times they have had together, or the positive contributions the afflicted patient has had in shaping them. It may take many reminders of who their loved one was in his prime. It might help to let your family and fellow caregivers understand your own struggle with accepting the new reality.

You are all embarking on a new relationship with the stricken member of your family. The old expectations are no longer valid. The Alzheimer's sufferer has his or her own fears of diminished functioning and of being rejected. You are all in a period of earth-shaking transition. How your family approaches these changes will have a major impact on their relationships with both you and the one who is wrestling with Alzheimer's. It will be a new relationship, to be sure, but, with caring and effort, it can be a deeply satisfying one.

CHAPTER SIX

Guiding Principles and Successful Approaches

As caregivers, we have every reason to feel sad and alone. We have every reason to slip into the mode of "poor me." We seem to have so little control over the basic facts of our situation, and the basic facts are not encouraging. Yet there is one thing we *always* have control over, something that no person or diagnosis or disease can take away from us, and that is the power to control our minds and hearts.

I have mentioned that during this period I read many books about the Holocaust. My friends were surprised that I was not reading something light or funny or uplifting, but I wanted books that would give me a sense of perspective. Immersion in these books reminded me of what real suffering was. My thoughts often returned to the words of psychiatrist Viktor Frankl, survivor of the Nazi death camps. In *Man's Search for Meaning,* Frankl wrote, "The thing no one can take away from us is the right to choose our attitude."

These words served as a constant reminder. I had a choice!

When it came to my outlook, my attitude, I was in charge. The understanding that I had even the *possibility* of shaping my response was enormously comforting. In Tal Ben-Shahar's book *Choose the Life You Want* he writes, "Research in psychology illustrates that about 40 percent of our happiness is determined by the choices that we make—what we choose *to do* and how we choose to *think* directly impact the way we *feel.*"

I believe in our power to control and to change our inner response, because I have experienced that power. I offer these guiding principles in the belief that our attitude and inner mindset is, in fact, the single most important resource at our command for shaping not only the life of our loved one going forward, but our own lives as well.

GUIDING PRINCIPLES

Here are three general principles, followed by the more specific suggestions based on these principles.

"Fight the Disease, Not the Journey"

I read or heard those words when Ady was first diagnosed, and I jotted them down because they sounded interesting: "Fight the disease, not the journey." At the time, I did not really understand what they meant, but gradually the concept became clearer.

The first part is obvious: we must fight the disease with every weapon we possess or uncover. We cannot take a back seat and watch the decline unfold. We must fight with full power and intelligence to provide the best physical and mental health possible, whether through new and ever-expanding medications, bringing more doctors into the loop, seeking appropriate help books, providing daily aerobic activity with a trainer or daily walks or a swim, or learning from others' experiences in many different ways.

The journey is a far different matter. The journey, I came to understand, is the emotional side of the equation. It means drawing on all our inner resources to make the final years together as beautiful as they can be. It means remembering the love of past years and not trashing it now with annoyance, frustration, impatience, bitterness, or self-pity. It means being aware every minute that your loved one did not choose this condition—for themselves or for you. It means reaching deep within yourself to empathize with what your patient is going through. If their memory fails them, we can connect to how we feel when our own memory slips, when we forget the name of someone we know well—the frustration and annoyance with ourselves and the doubt and uncertainty about our own minds. We can magnify those feelings many times over, imagining this loss as a constant state, imagining what it must be like to feel diminished countless times a day, to have to depend on others for virtually everything when you're used to running your own life. In doing so, we lay the foundations of empathy.

As some faculties are lost, new heightened qualities can reveal themselves. These, too, can seem like challenges at first, but they can also be opportunities. Yes, Ady's memory was slipping—but I found that his emotional sensitivity was greatly heightened. He reacted with uncanny awareness to the slightest hint of disappointment in me. He crumbled with a raised eyebrow or sharp intake of breath. I had to learn to refrain from any body language that suggested disappointment. This was far from easy, but it became easier with time. After all, this was the man with whom I had spent close to three-quarters of my life. If you are fortunate enough to be in a good marriage, there are harder jobs than giving your mate the abundance of love and appreciation and care he deserves. If your marriage is not ideal, this can be an opportunity to change the tone of the relationship.

The rewards of positive reinforcement were startling. I am convinced that the reason for Ady's peace of mind and wonderful smile is that he was surrounded, not by disappointment, judgment, and annoyance but by respect and appreciation and an abiding love—from me, from his children, from friends, and even from the best of the caregivers that he needed in the last few years (whom he thanked a hundred times a day). People may experience loss of memory, of movement, of balance, of inhibitions and control, but they know instinctively when they are loved.

As time went on, I began to realize that I was getting great satisfaction out of my new role. More and more, I discovered that those old thoughts of, "Why is this difficult, ugly disease happening to my husband? To me?" were being replaced by feelings of satisfaction for being able to give him all the warmth he craved.

So today I would word the adage differently: Fight the disease. *Embrace* the journey. Embracing the journey invites you to use every bit of creativity to find ways to help your mate be the best he now can be; to encourage him to try areas he never ventured into before; to reinforce abilities that have lain dormant—with a musical instrument, with drawing, with singing or dancing; to believe that quality of life is still possible; to harness all the residual good, in yourself and your loved one, and bring it to the fore.

This can be a difficult approach to accept. In the months after Ady's diagnosis, I found a rare guide book expressing the notion that life with your afflicted loved one could be deeply gratifying, even a time to explore new avenues, and a time of creativity. At the time, that sounded so preposterous that I was furious. These books were often written by doctors who had, I thought, no experience living with a spouse afflicted with Alzheimer's. Why would they give such false hope? How could they make such Pollyannaish statements without living through it themselves? How could this possibly be a happy time? I apologize for my lack of faith. Over the years, this initially terrifying period turned into a tranquil, nurturing time of exploration and discovery. It became a time of peace and acceptance.

. . .

The concrete approaches that I describe in the following chapters are by no means guarantees. Yet, if initiated in the early stages, before negative behavior is entrenched, they can potentially make a powerful difference—if not in the progress of the disease, then at least in your quality of lives, as individuals and together. Books on Alzheimer's and dementia often describe the caregiver as having debilitating feelings of helplessness. My experience during the early stages was that even though I *felt* powerless to make the kind of difference that would stop or slow the disease, I was clearly not helpless. It is hugely empowering to understand that one might be able to alter the outcome. The chapter that follows describes some of the methodology I learned over time, through many trials and many mistakes, methodology that made my husband's life—and my own!—richer, happier, and more content.

I understand that my experience was not typical. Not all Alzheimer's patients can make the degree of progress that Ady achieved. So much of the credit goes to him. I am quite sure I would not have been capable of the calm and acceptance that Ady displayed, no matter how loving and supportive the people around me were. For Ady it was more than resignation. He embraced his life and made the most of every day. My respect for Ady's handling the changes in his life with such grace moved me to the core. The patterns established throughout a marriage that kept getting better with time allowed us to continue to interact with each other in ways that brought each of us unexpected gratification. I received the greatest satisfaction and yes, even joy, knowing that I was helping to create the fertile soil that permitted him to thrive. What he experienced from me was not a phony smile but a deep inner contentment and pride for the progress we were achieving together.

The Power of Decisions

I have long thought that the real "action" in life is not the "doing" but the decision to do.

We decide to take a vacation. After that we choose where and when—whether it is to be a road trip, a visit to another city, a cruise, and how many days we will be away. Most think of that as the planning stage and the going itself as the "action."

I see it differently. The real action *is* the decision. Making the initial big decision is the hard part. Once that is done, all the subsequent ones become routine. We book the hotel or the ship or contact the family or friends that we hope to stay with. We find ourselves thinking about what to bring. We pack. On the appointed day we go to the airport or begin our drive. We hopefully have a delightful trip. We are left with our memories and return to our lives. None of this would be possible without the mental choice we made.

The scenario just described is a onetime decision. However, I believe we tend to be guided by the overarching principles we have consciously chosen, and that adhering to those principles has the potential to make subsequent decisions—any of which may seem challenging at the time—enormously easier. Throughout, I've written of our ability to shape our reaction to the reality we face. We often fail to appreciate the power we have in virtually every situation to determine how we will behave or even as Viktor Frankl said, "the right to choose our attitude."

Way back on that first day at the Wien Center, when sitting in the waiting room while Ady was being tested, I wrote of my determination to make the remaining years we had together good and sweet and joyful for as long as possible. I unwittingly made one of the biggest decisions of my life. I didn't realize then that all my subsequent efforts to be kind, caring, creative, and sensitive were in a sense following through on that early decision. Looking back, I begin to understand that my intuitive resolution powerfully shaped the next six years of our lives. Determining the highest principles by which we wish to proceed frees us from the need to revisit the overarching decision, leaving only the need to reevaluate daily situations to choose a specific course of action.

Value of Keeping a Journal

I began what inadvertently became a journal. I found my insights came at the most unexpected times. Wishing I had a piece of paper at the doctor's office or hunting for some blank space in a concert program in order to jot down a thought, I eventually learned to carry in my purse a tiny notepad. I tried, not always successfully, to remember to transcribe my scribbled notes to my computer.

I did not have the remotest thought in those early days of writing a book. Writing everything down was simply a tool to remind myself of what worked and what did not. But I soon understood that the journal also became a record of my thoughts and feelings. There is something quite powerful about expressing one's thoughts either in writing or to a therapist. Unexpressed feelings become a weight, an intangible sense of fear or horror. Once expressed, the perspective changes. For me, the vague sensation of fear eroded. It enabled me to define the issues and to formulate concrete plans to deal with them. Writing helped me go from the disquieting feeling of unease to perceiving a problem in need of a solution. Writing may also be extremely helpful to those who are experiencing loneliness and isolation.

Creating Sweet Times

I tried to create sweet times—to use our time together productively. Whenever we were in the car for our many trips to doctors, I would encourage Ady to sing all the many, many songs that he knew. It always amazed me that the lyrics would come tumbling back to him, whether in simple songs like "Foggy, Foggy Dew" or "If I Loved You" from *Carousel* (he knew the words to all the long verses), or in the many Dartmouth songs that he used to sing in the glee club. Driving together became a happy time, rather than a time of drudgery. Music, in any form, brought much joy into his life and made connections in his brain that surpassed all others.

I was delighted to learn of a superb movie called *Alive Inside* that corroborates the connection between music and memory. It was released in late 2015, four years after Ady passed away. The video shows dozens of cases of residents in nursing homes who appear to have lost all contact with the world. Many had not responded or spoken a word in years. It shows the initial struggles

Ady, in his final year, at our son Mark's wedding

to attempt to awaken memory—without success. Then earphones were placed on the patient with music their family members thought might be appropriate. The patient's reaction is indescribable. It usually began with a look of shock. Their eyes open wide; their head is no longer drooping on their chest. A broad smile emerges. Some tap fingers or feet along with the beat, others sing out loud, often with accurate words. One woman, who had not walked in years, got out of her wheelchair and began to dance, with a smile that transported her back to another era. The music awakened something deep in these patients that had been presumed lost; it awakened feelings they had not felt in years. Music seems to involve a different part of the brain than words alone. The goal of the research was to try to introduce music into nursing homes. If you'd like more information, go to www.aliveinside.us or search for "Dan Cohen Music and Memory."

I also used our time in the car, when I had Ady all to myself with no distractions, to say the many things that I did not want to leave unsaid. My father died at age eighty-five, ten years after having a stroke that left half of him paralyzed. Fortunately, my dad's mind (which was constantly stimulated) remained intact. The death of a loved one is always difficult, and one is never really ready, but I understood that it was easier for me because nothing between us was left unsaid. I had expressed all the love I felt for my dad many times, in many ways. Remembering those feelings, I consciously tried to make productive use of the precious gift of time Ady and I still had together. I tried to make this a time of giving love, in a way that was admittedly vastly different from the past but still satisfying and rewarding to us both. A tender touch of the cheek or pat on the arm goes a long way to make someone feel appreciated and whole. Current Alzheimer's research acknowledges that feelings of loneliness and isolation contribute to worsening of the condition. Praise and acknowledgement of something remembered or done well contributes to a feeling of well-being.

SUCCESSFUL APPROACHES

Although I had made the mental decision to try to choose joy, I didn't have the slightest idea how to achieve it. I walked with a tentative step at first. All I had was a motivating goal: to keep this a positive, loving time for both of us for as long as possible. I soaked up everything I could learn. I became super-sensitive to how every action on my part affected Ady. But mostly I observed and learned from others. My mother, who learned from everyone, used to tell me: "When I am in a fish store, I learn about fish." The memory of that guidance must have stayed with me. Moving in a foreign country, desperately trying to learn a new language, I learned both from traditional sources and from the most unlikely. Whenever I had a new insight, I scribbled it down as a guide for myself. Most important, when I observed a way of dealing with a situation that worked, I didn't think of it as applying only to that particular situation. I tried to identify the positive principle behind it, so I could apply it to other situations. Here are some of the principles I embraced.

"Not Now" versus "Never"

Before Ady was officially diagnosed with Alzheimer's at age seventy-five, he began getting confused while driving on familiar routes. After a few mild fender-benders, my great concern became, "How do I get Ady to give up driving?" I remembered when Ady and his sisters tried to take away his mother's car, long after it was clearly dangerous for herself and others for her to be behind the wheel. She said, "If you take my car away, I'll kill myself." To my horror, they let her drive.

I have related that, as my concerns began to mount, Ady and I went to see Dr. Ellen Rees, a brilliant and caring psychiatrist. At our first visit Dr. Rees explained that she had no idea what was going on with Ady—whether his symptoms were psychological or physical. She suggested that Ady go through a battery of neurological tests. After receiving the results, the doctors put him on Aricept and Namenda, the classic medications to improve memory. When we returned to Dr. Rees's office I brought up the issue of Ady's driving. Dr. Rees turned to him and said, in the most matter-of-fact tone, "Ady, you're on some new medication. Perhaps it would be a good idea, until you see how the medication affects you, not to drive for a while."

That simple statement made sense to Ady. "For a while" was not forever; he responded positively immediately. For the next month either I or one of the caretakers at our home took Ady wherever he wanted to go and picked him up afterwards. I believe that he was inwardly relieved, because he occasionally got lost in familiar places and sensed he was having trouble. He liked being chauffeured around. About a month later, when someone casually asked him if he was driving home from the concert, I heard Ady answer simply: "No. I don't drive anymore." I took a deep breath and tried to hide my enormous relief. It was such an easy and successful conclusion to what I had anticipated would be a major battle.

It was also a powerful lesson for me: "Not now" is so much easier to accept than "Never." I applied it whenever possible.

Question versus Command

Another lesson came from observing someone else—someone who had no formal training. Lizette Rodriguez, originally our housekeeper, became Ady's chief caregiver during the last two and a half years after he fractured his hip. During those years she was at his side—and mine—for most of the hours in the day. Lizette was loving and instinctively wise. She never had a day's training as an aide, but her innate wisdom and deep caring surpassed anything that a course or book might have taught. She had worked with our family for about fifteen years before Ady was diagnosed and had deep respect and affection for him. I learned so very much from observing her ways with Ady.

After attending to Ady's morning medication and bathroom routine, it would have been perfectly reasonable and lovely for Lizette to announce, in an upbeat, cheery voice, "Mr. Berger, your breakfast is ready!" She never did that. Instead, Lizette always asked, "Mr. Berger, are you ready for breakfast?"

He would respond with a resounding, "Yes!"

The difference was crucial. The first statement is an implied command: no matter how sweetly it is said, the message is still, "Your breakfast is ready. You have to come and eat now." The second statement allowed the decision to be his. He was given a choice! My jaw dropped with delight at the lesson I learned.

Watching Lizette closely, I began to notice that she never told Ady what to do. Instead, she always asked a question. "Would you like to go to the bathroom before we get in the car?" "Would you prefer to go on the stationary bicycle, or to take your walk now?" She always empowered Ady to make his own decisions, instinctively enabling him to retain his dignity.

Observing how wonderfully this simple technique worked, I, too, began to phrase everything in the form of a question. "Would you like to draw now—or do a Sudoku problem before we begin the movie?" I would hand him three movies, each of which I knew he'd enjoy, and ask, "Which one would you like to watch?" My questions were within the confines of what needed to be accomplished. Whatever choice he made was fine with me. He liked making the decisions and owned them once he did. Presenting these options in the form of a question, rather than a command, had consistently magical results.

Responding to Oft-Repeated Questions

Though every case is different, certain aspects of dementia and Alzheimer's are classic. Hard as one tries, these symptoms are difficult, perhaps even impossible, to change. How we choose to *react* to those behaviors, however, is entirely within our power. Do we react with annoyance, or with acceptance and support?

One of the most universally known symptoms is that the patient asks the same question over and over again, forgetting the answer a few minutes later. Early on, when Ady asked "Where are you going tonight?" for the fifth time, I did what everyone does. I responded with an intake of breath, or a raised eyebrow, or closing my eyes, or with some other nonverbal expression that said, *I've told you that a hundred times.* I then spoke as calmly as I could. "I'm going with Elaine to the ballet."

The words themselves were fine, but the damage done in an instant by my nonverbal response could not be undone. My initial raised eyebrow was like a punch in the gut. Ady felt diminished. He was disappointed in himself. As soon as I said it, he remembered that he had already asked.

Watching this reaction, I wrote in my journal that I was determined not to respond ever again with even a hint of annoyance. When frustration crept in, as it is bound to when the same question is asked over and over again, I learned to tell myself: *He would not be asking if he remembered.*

That one simple thought helped me react with compassion and tenderness rather than with frustration and annoyance. I learned to respond for the eighth time with the same love and kindness as I had the first: "Sweetie, I'm going to the ballet with Elaine," often giving Ady a loving pat on the cheek or taking his hand. It was one of the most difficult decisions for me to carry out. But the results were so reinforcing. His response was always loving and appreciative.

Avoiding Confrontation

One of the aides, who was not with us very long, got Ady hooked on one of her favorite TV programs, *Judge Judy.* Ady watched it with her every day. When she was no longer with us, the habit continued. He absolutely had to watch it every day. One might feel that if watching *Judge Judy* made him happy, let it be! But I had too much faith in Ady to see him take a full hour out of his precious day watching people fight over problems that were of no concern to us. I tried everything I could to wean him from the show. I appealed to his intellect. "Ady, do you really care what happens to these people?" I explained that it was eating into his exercise or napping time. (His days were so full and so programmed with necessities, as I'll describe later, that he truly did not have an extra hour to spend during the day.) We were having daily arguments, each of us adamant in our position.

Finally, one day, I tried a new approach. "Okay, Ady. How long do you want to watch?"

He answered immediately: "Five minutes!" Every day, without my saying a word, he watched the program for five minutes and then turned it off himself, with no reminder from me, until he eventually lost interest. The battle was over.

This simple resolution was another potent lesson for me—a principle I continued to apply to virtually every situation. I tried never again to confront Ady, to insist on or demand what had to be accomplished, but rather to work it out with him, like a team pulling in the same direction. With one exception, which I describe in the following section, I avoided confrontation and always gave him a face-saving way out if he didn't want to do something.

The benefits to this approach were more than just avoiding confrontation. Ady truly had a hand in so many of the solutions we worked out. I believe that the total lack of confrontation and his genuine role in finding the solutions allowed him to keep his dignity and feel in control—and helped us to avoid the classic Alzheimer's anger. We were becoming, again, the partners that we had been all our married lives.

Taking Charge While Consulting

The reality is that when an Alzheimer's patient is incapable of making crucial decisions, the caregiver has no choice but to take over that role. *How* you take over, however, makes all the difference. It can determine whether you have a contented, cooperative, happy loved one, or a diminished and angry one.

The most difficult confrontation Ady and I ever had was over who would take charge of his medication. People in their later years often take a lot of medication. Ady certainly did: medication for his lungs, blood pressure, Alzheimer's; blood thinners and more—a daily total of thirty-one pills (plus special pills like antibiotics as needed) and eleven inhaler and lung treatments.

Taking such a quantity of prescription medication each day meant that meticulous monitoring was essential. Without a flawless system, it would be virtually impossible even for a person with full faculties to remember whether a particular pill had been taken or not. Ady's medications were especially critical, since an under- or overdose of medications like Coumadin or Prednisone could be life threatening. His medication schedule was further complicated by the fact that the dosage of some of his medications varied from week to week, depending on his condition or that week's blood tests.

Ady had been in total charge of his medication all his life. On various hospital stays, years before the Alzheimer's diagnosis, he would panic when he was not permitted to monitor his own medications. A nurse would enter his room with a little plastic cup filled with unrecognizable medications—usually generic, which he did not take. Not having witnessed the pills come out of their labeled bottles and having no idea what he was taking, he would get unnerved and agitated, and with good reason.

Taking that role out of his hands was far more difficult than taking away his right to drive, but as his condition progressed, it was clear that my taking over was essential. Ady's health and life were on the line. About three years into Ady's diagnosis, I told our son, Mark, of my new concern that his dad was often unsure whether he had taken a pill. Mark advised me that I had no choice and simply had to monitor his medication. He suggested that I switch to one of those large weekly pill cases with four compartments per day (breakfast, lunch, dinner, bedtime).

Ady had not used these pill containers in the past. Every time he needed medication, he opened each pill bottle as needed. When his mind was sharp, he was very precise. It may not have been the best system, but it worked. When I brought up the new methodology, his rebellion was fierce. His medications were his domain! He was not about to give up control. He was not about to make a change. He understood and admitted in all other areas that his memory was slipping. But his medication was sacred.

The first foolproof (thought I) tactic I attempted was, "Mark suggested that we use this pillbox."

It didn't work. "I'll call Mark and tell him I won't do that."

Mark happened to be on vacation that week, so I tried another tactic, applying the strategy of "Not now versus never."

"Dear, I don't want to bother Mark on his vacation. Until he comes back next week, let's try using this pillbox together. I'll help you open the medication bottles, and you select every pill that goes in. Let's see if you are comfortable with that until Mark gets home." That approach seemed reasonable to Ady. He understood that he was not giving up any control in selecting and seeing what medications went into each little compartment in the pillbox.

So we set up the week's pills together. It took about forty minutes. Ady instructed me on every pill and watched me put it in the correct spot. I had, years before, begun drawing up an ever-changing daily medication chart for him. The chart was in two parts: The first part—for us all, especially the doctors, to understand the overall schedule—listed all his medications and how many times a day each pill or treatment was taken. The aides, or whoever was administering the medication, usually referred to the second part of the chart, looking at the specific time of day to know what was required at that time. Lizette and I also used the second part of the chart as an essential guide every time we set up his weekly pills. (A sample of that chart is shown on pp. 74–75.)

Ady could simply look at the correct hour or time slot of the day to know what to take or do next. That medication chart and his daily schedule charts became so essential that we referred to them as "the Bibles."

By the end of the first week, Ady recognized the wisdom of our new system and felt comfortable. He directed it. He liked not having to struggle opening the small pill bottles, which were becoming more difficult for him to do. He liked not having to worry whether he missed a pill. For several months we set out the pills together, one week at a time. He enjoyed having me with him as we made a "date" every Sunday morning to do the week's medication. It became a sweet time. He liked having my full attention and the feeling of security that it brought.

Then, one Sunday, when I asked if he was ready to select the pills, he responded, "I'd really rather take a nap now. Will you do it?" He had the confidence that I would do it correctly, and, most important, he made that decision himself. I don't recall that he ever did the medication with me again.

That does not mean that he ever really relinquished responsibility. About a year later, when I placed his dinner medication on

ADY DAILY MEDICATION:

Doctors: Ady is NOT to take: CIPRO, LEVAQUIN, or AVALOX due to the effect on his Achilles tendon
NOTE: Items highlighted IN YELLOW are medications with changing doses as per Dr's instructions
BLUE = NOT a PILL
BLACK = IN WEEKLY PILL BOX

GENERAL DAILY MEDICATION:

Medication	Times per day	When	Notes
Nebulizer Xopenex 0-63Mg + MUCOMYST (Acetylcysteine 10% vial)	3		
ADVAIR 500/50	2	With nebulizer treatment	
SPIRIVA HandiHaler Oral Inhalation	1	With nebulizer treatment	
VEST Routine, acapella, etc.	2	With nebulizer treatment	
NASACORT or FLONASE nasal spray 50 mcg	1		
GAVISCON before breakfast	2		
ENALAPRIL MALEATE 10 mg 12/19/08	1		
stopped LOTREL 5/20 mg on 12/19/08	0		
stopped SUDAFED on Mar 2, 2009	0		
LASIX 40 mg 5 days, 60 mg Tues & Fri	1		
CALAN 120 mg	2		
ZYLOPRIM 100 mg	1		
NAMENDA MEMANTINE HCl tablets 10 mg	2		
LEXAPRO 10 mg	1		
PREDNISONE as of July 2006		5 mg daily (2.5 mg breakfast & 2.5 mg dinner)	
PREDNISONE as of Sept 09		7.5 (5 mg AM, 2.5 dinner)	
ECOTRIN 81 mg	1		
POTASSIUM CL 10 meq	2		
MUCINEX	2		
CoQ 10 ST	1		
ACIDOPHILOS	1		
Men's One A Day	1		
Vitamin C 500 mg	1		
CALTRATE 600mg + D	2		
PROVIGIL 200 mg	1		
FLEET ENEMA every day			
CARAFATE (SUCRALFATE 1 gm)	2		
NEXIUM 40 mg	1		
COUMADIN (dose varies) begun on 4/17/06	2	40 mg 5 days, 60 mg Tues & Fri	

WHEN EACH MEDICATION IS TO BE TAKEN

Medication	When	Notes
AM or AFTER BREAKFAST		
NEBULIZER XOPENEX 0-63 mg + MUCOMYST (Acetylcysteine 10% vial)	before breakfast	

ADVAIR 500/50	after breakfast
SPIRIVA HandiHaler Oral Inhalation	after breakfast
VEST Routine, acapella,etc.	after breakfast
NASACORT or FLONASE nasal spray 50 mcg	after breakfast
GAVISCON	after breakfast
stopped SUDAFED on Mar 2, 2009	
LASIX 40 mg 5 days, 60 mg Tues & Fri	after breakfast
CALAN 120 mg	after breakfast
ZYLOPRIM 100 mg	after breakfast
NAMENDA MEMANTINE HCl tablets 10 mg	after breakfast
LEXAPRO 10 Mg	after breakfast
PREDNISONE (dose varies each week)	after breakfast
ECOTRIN 81 mg	after breakfast
POTASSIUM CL 10 meq	after breakfast
MUCINEX (3/24/06)	after breakfast
CoQ 10 ST	after breakfast
ACIDOPHILOS	after breakfast
FLEET ENEMA DAILY	after breakfast
Vitamin C 500 mg	after breakfast
Men's One A Day	after breakfast
BONIVA (last Saturday each month)	after breakfast

MIDDAY

CALTRATE 600mg + D	about 12 noon
NEBULIZER XOPENEX 0-63 mg + MUCOMYST (Acetylcysteine 10% vial)	before nap
PROVIGIL 200 mg	about 5:30 pm

AFTER DINNER

PREDNISONE	current: 3 mg 6 days, 4 mg Fri
COUMADIN (dose varies) begun on 4/17/06	40 mg 5 days, 60 mg Tues & Fri
CALAN 120 mg	after dinner
MUCINEX (3/24/06)	after dinner
POTASSIUM CL 10 meq	after dinner
CALTRATE 600mg + D	after dinner
CARAFATE (SUCRALFATE 1 gm)	after dinner

BEDTIME

NEBULIZER XOPENEX 0-63mg +	bedtime	
MUCOMYST (Acetylcysteine 10% vial)	bedtime	
ADVAIR 500/50	bedtime	
VEST TREATMENT	bedtime	
LIPITOR 10 mg	bedtime	
TOPAMAX 50 mg	bedtime	(begun instead of Mysoline)
GAVISCON	bedtime	
ARICEPT 10 mg	bedtime	
NAMENDA MEMANTINE HCl tablets 10 mg	bedtime	
TRAZODONE 50 mg	bedtime	

a plate at the dining room table, as we did each night, he looked down at the plate and said, "You're missing a pill. There are only five here. There are supposed to be six." He was absolutely right. Since his Prednisone dosage varied each week according to the doctor's instructions, I had left out the pill until getting that week's prescribed dosage from the doctor. Unbeknownst to me, mathematically inclined as he was, he had been silently checking up on me every day. Of course, I heaped praise on him for his important catch, and Ady beamed that great Ady smile.

To preclude my making further mistakes, I trained Lizette to work beside me and understand how to select his complicated medication as well. Lizette would occasionally catch me in an error. I never allowed anyone else to take over that responsibility, but it was comforting for me to know that in case of emergency, Lizette was totally competent to handle the medications. Ady had complete trust that his medication was being handled well, but he always kept a watchful eye in his own way.

That initial medication argument was a wonderful teacher. After that I tried never to make a unilateral decision for Ady. Even if the issue was critically important (as the pills were) and I was clear about what the end result had to be, I always consulted him, so that he felt that he owned the decision. What I learned was to try never to confront or insist or demand even those things that I knew had to be accomplished. This resolution colored all our interactions, as we each became more skilled in working together. It was no longer me telling him what he had to do. We worked together as a team toward a common goal.

The reward for both of us was major. Instead of following the usual path of an Alzheimer's patient in becoming more and more combative, Ady became more agreeable, more trusting, and vastly more appreciative. His inner sense of security and well-being continued to grow. He constantly expressed his deep appreciation—verbally, in writing, and in countless other tangible ways.

Establishing a Consistent Routine

The unexpected rattled Ady and threw him off balance. He functioned with greater confidence and peace when his routine was predictable. We had charts all over his bathroom indicating what would happen every minute of the day. When was his doctor's appointment? What time did he need to leave for the appointment? When was his physical therapist arriving? The daily charts spelled out every slot: mealtime, naptime, treatment time, exercise time. This may sound rigid, but in fact it gave him a deep sense of security. For a short while we had a very capable physical therapist who was only able to fit Ady in as her schedule permitted. This proved completely unworkable. Her times varied each day. Ady found this disorienting. He needed consistency in his life. We had to find someone else who could come at the same time five days a week.

The key is to try to closely observe how your spouse is reacting to the decisions you both have made. If the answer is "not well," be flexible and change them!

Maintaining a Calm Atmosphere

As I observed the disconcerting confusion Ady experienced over even the simplest tasks, I attempted to simplify his world. Any distraction caused discomfort. He would literally jump at any sharp or sudden noise. He seemed to have a heightened awareness of any tension in the room and was thrown off balance by it. In a calm, quiet, and predictable environment, he did well.

Ady needed to spend a lot of time in the bathroom for various lung treatments. For years, we had kept a television in the bathroom, so he could watch the news. Now it took him twenty-five minutes to brush his teeth because he was so mesmerized by the TV. He was simply not able to do two things at once. When I suggested removing the television from his bathroom, he rebelled but promised not to watch it. It was irresistible, however, and he would flip it on whenever I left the room and give me an impish grin when I returned and found it on.

The ultimate solution was not complicated. Years before, I had made a two-and-a-half-hour iPod playlist of most of his favorite classical music. I replaced the television with the iPod. Instead of turning on the TV when he entered his bathroom, he automatically flipped on the classical music. The music was soothing and comforting, and yet it stimulated his mind. It kept him smiling and relaxed. He never asked for the television again. I'm not sure he even noticed it was gone.

This raises another important principle. So often I found that the solutions to avoiding confrontation or irritability were the same as those we use parenting children. We don't take an inappropriate toy away without replacing it with a substitute. Now, as caregivers, we can employ the same strategy we may have used as parents: if you have to take something away, try to replace it with something even better.

Planning Extra Time

Perhaps the greatest difficulty we had in the early years was my own unrealistic expectation that Ady was still capable of managing his time. I didn't understand at first that he could no longer accomplish a simple task (like dressing) in the same amount of time that he did in the past. In the early days, when he was habitually late for doctor's appointments, we would leave with me being angry. Ady would visibly shrink before me. It was awful. Fortunately, that period did not last long enough to do damage. I soon accepted the sad reality: *He can't.* Once I accepted that "Ady would if he could," I was able to help him plan for every event with a realistic schedule. If it took him two hours to get ready for a doctor's appointment or a concert, I began to get him ready two hours before leaving. As I took over the job of planning time realistically, our arguments about being on time ceased. I was no longer angry if he was not successful. Ady was calmer; I was as well. It was a crucial change for both of us.

One Thing at a Time

One of the ways to keep a calm atmosphere for Ady was to do one thing at a time. This is not easy for me; I'm a multitasker and much happier if I can accomplish several things at once. Ady was always more comfortable without distractions, and that trait became vastly more pronounced during his years with Alzheimer's. Most Alzheimer's patients, unsure and confused and slightly disoriented as they are, cannot contemplate doing two things at once without extreme agitation. As much as he loved classical music, he could not hear it playing if he were reading a newspaper or attempting to work at his desk. For him it was like trying to read two books simultaneously. I observed that more than one thing at a time—music or someone talking when he was concentrating on something else—disoriented him and created confusion. Although not always possible, I'd try not to interrupt him, even with a simple question, when he was otherwise engaged. The goal was to create a calm, quiet atmosphere in which he could thrive.

Creating a Sense of Order

I tried to achieve and maintain a sense of order in the house. To eliminate the unexpected, we posted daily routines on the mirrors, including aide schedules that showed which aide would be on and at what time. If we had evening plans, they too were posted: the event, the time, what time we had to leave, and who would be joining us. At all times, I attempted to make life as stable as possible and to reduce the opportunity for confusion.

We used different schedule charts, depending on where we were and whether it was a weekday or weekend. An example of one of the daily charts we depended on—a late-stage schedule, showing how refined the charts became—is shown on the following pages. This refinement took time; it was not achieved overnight but refined continuously for years. The yellow highlights were to alert the aides to a medication time.

There were different similar schedules for weekdays and weekends, if we were going out at night, and if there was a daytime activity like a doctor's appointment. Unusual events like doctors' appointments and evening plans were posted separately, each with the people we were seeing, the time of our appointment, and what time we had to leave.

Deciding When to Supply Answers

Memory is a funny thing. It goes in and out. I suspect this is true to some degree for all of us as we get older. How many times do we momentarily forget the name of a person we know well, and then, suddenly, it's there? That slippage is greatly exaggerated in one who has Alzheimer's. One moment something was there with Ady; the next, something he clearly knew five minutes before was gone—then, just as suddenly, in another context, was back again. Once I understood this, the question became how to deal with it.

Balance became the rule for me. On the one hand, I didn't want to jump in with an answer that I was fairly sure he knew. I didn't want to become his brain, so that he stopped thinking for himself. On the other hand, I wanted to be careful not to frustrate him and cause discomfort if the answer was not readily his. I found that coming in through the side door with a small hint that triggered

Sample Chart Ady Schedule Weekday (2010–2011)

Medications highlighted in YELLOW

8:00 AM	Prepare Ady's breakfast
8:15 AM	Wake & while still in bed:
	Eat one half banana
	Take Prednisone – Gaviscon
	Back-stretching exercises (3 positions)
	In bathroom:
	Change to dry clothes, undershirt & bathrobe & slipper socks
9:00 AM	Breakfast
	MEDICATION (pills in AM pill box)
9:50 AM	In bathroom:
	1. Fleet enema
	Stay on toilet for:
	2. Nasacort or Flonase
	3. Spiriva
	4. Avair
	5. Floss
	6. Shave
10:30 AM	Shower
	(After shower: A & D ointment on bottom; Depends & undershirt)
	Water Pik and brush teeth
10:45 AM	Nebulizer treatment
	(During treatment: lotion on arms & legs)
11:20 AM	Vest treatment
	During vest treatment:
	Lotion on face
	Support hose on
	Sneakers on
	Finish dressing

11:40 AM	MEDICATION: 1 CARAFATE in NOON pill box
11:45 AM	Go down to gym in Building 1
	Stationary bicycle until physical therapist arrives
12 noon–1:00 PM	Marge (physical therapy) Monday–Friday
12:45 PM	Aide to be in GYM to pick Ady up and bring home at 1:00
1:20 PM (approx)	Bathroom
	Then watch "All My Children" in office while eating lunch at desk
	Water pik & brush teeth
2:00 PM	Nap
3:00 PM	Walk or swim
5:00 PM	MEDICATION: 1 CARAFATE + 1 NEXIUM in NOON pill box
5:00 PM	Play piano
5:45 PM	If time: Computer or watch Metropolitan Opera on computer
6:00 PM	NEBULIZER TREATMENT
6:20 PM	Dinner & MEDICATION in Evening pill box
7:30 PM	Write, draw, or Sudoku at dinner table
7:45 PM	Watch TV selected movie
8:30 PM	In bathroom:
	1. Floss teeth & water pik
	2. ADVAIR
	3. NEBULIZER
	4. Brush teeth
	5. VEST TREATMENT
	6. MEDICATION in Bedtime pill box
10:00 PM	To sleep!

the answer was often a good tactic. "Remember, they stopped by at the concert last night to say hello," or "His first name begins with a *B.*" Ady would beam when he got it. Other times I'd ask, "Do you want me to tell you, or do you want to think about it?" He usually gave me a definite answer, either, "Let me think," or "Tell me." I always respected his answer and never tried to coax.

Most importantly, I strove *never* to show frustration or disappointment, never to imply an incredulous sense of *How could you forget that?* This was difficult for me because each lapse in memory was a fresh reminder of his condition. Again, I remembered my golden rule: ACCEPTANCE is key. No judgment, only a loving smile. It was not easy, but for me it worked, and the resulting happy partner was all the reward I needed.

A more frustrating issue for me arose during dinner "conversation." (I use the word in quotes because it was a far cry from our former dinners, when we truly talked about our day, how we felt, what we were proud of or disappointed about, the world, politics, our lives, our children and grandchildren. Our dinner talk now was mostly about games and puzzles.) The dilemma for me was that no matter what I said, Ady's first response was always, "What?" At first, I was exasperated at hearing the same immediate response over and over. Then I began to understand: It took Ady a while, now, to digest and process the words I spoke. "What?" was simply a way for him to buy time. Once I understood this, I began—while trying to avoid any trace of annoyance in my voice—to say, "Dear, tell me what you did grasp from what I just said." His response, almost always, indicated that he had understood the essence of what I had said. He simply needed more time to process it.

Once I understood what was going on, it became easier to give him the praise for understanding what I said the first time. I learned to speak slowly and distinctly, giving him the time he needed to absorb the words but careful never to talk down to him or speak to him as if he were a child. I tried to never lose sight of how intelligent Ady had been. His memory was severely diminished—but his feelings were not. If anything, he had a heightened sense of the emotions I conveyed, both deliberately and inadvertently. I tried to offer him a safe conversational space, along with plenty of encouragement for the excellent advances that he made.

Managing Unwanted Behavior

Whenever I hoped to change negative or inappropriate behavior, I realized that if I began my conversation with words that sounded critical, Ady simply shut down. I learned, when I had something important to convey, to begin with endearing and positive words, accompanied by my usual gentle touch on the cheek. I interspersed continuous acknowledgments of the wonderful person that he was. I tried to keep my tone supportive, never critical, letting him know that I was on his side. What I got back was not only his contented smile but someone who was ready to receive.

The unwritten rule that emerged for me was not to wait until typical unwanted Alzheimer's behavior became entrenched or unbearable to try to change it. Anything that did not return the love that I was putting forth was bad for me. I tried to change unwanted behavior at the first sign. Whatever I felt to be offensive was always discussed with kindness and with a sense of building together. With an occasional reminder, the inappropriate behavior towards me stopped. He wanted so deeply to please me, to keep me happy.

Years later, my philosophy of heading off the first sign of negative behavior was reinforced when I visited a lifelong friend in the hospital who was beyond anyone's ability to reach. He was delusional with a fever. I found him ranting with rage at everyone. He recognized me immediately and gave me a big smile, but then exploded in a tirade of anger against all those closest to him—

caregivers who were on the point of collapse, trying to deal with his demands and their own lack of sleep. I was totally unable to reach him. When I said, "I love you!" he responded, "I don't want to hear any speeches. Get me out of here. Everyone tells me what to do."

I was crushed. I describe this sad scene because I understood that at this point, none of the techniques I write about would have helped. He was too far gone with his fever and awareness of his own decline. Once anger becomes the automatic response of the patient, it is a very difficult habit to break. Unfortunately, as caregivers, we too often respond with our own anger, exhaustion, and frustration.

I took a dual approach. On the one hand, I was strict in not accepting any unwanted behavior. At the same time, I made it my mission to be *more* compassionate, *more* giving, *more* expressive of love—and probably more patient than I ever was, even in the best times of our previous lives together. My goal was to do everything in my power to help Ady keep his dignity, to give him the feeling that he had control of his life—and, at the same time, to help him be my partner in creating a life that was loving and joyful for us both.

Managing Inappropriate Public Behavior

Alzheimer's patients often lose their inhibitions. I began to get frequent reports from caring friends that my sweet, gentle, respected husband, who never spoke an off-color word all his life, was making sexual comments to women, in several cases asking a married woman with children if she were a virgin. Then I heard it myself. At a party, he said to a woman wearing a modestly low-cut dress, "I'm looking at your boobs."

I did not try to address this in public but waited until we returned home. (This is vital.) I remember clearly the conversation we had that night, which went pretty much like this. I'll call the woman Jane.

HELENE: Ady, do you have any idea how much I love you?
ADY: *Big smile.*
HELENE, *holding his hand tenderly, and with no trace of annoyance or criticism:* Sweetheart, I heard you say to Jane tonight, "I'm looking at your boobs."
ADY: *Guilty smile.*
HELENE: Dear, that's not you. It's embarrassing to Jane. It's embarrassing for you. And it's embarrassing for me. That's not the person I care about so much.
ADY: I'm sorry, dear.
HELENE: Let's not talk about what already happened. Let's look ahead. I'd like you to really try to avoid comments like that in the future.
ADY: I will.
HELENE: Let's come up with a code word just between us, to let you know when your behavior is inappropriate.
ADY, *after a few moments of thinking:* Good. Let's make the word: *inappropriate.*
HELENE: Wonderful. *(I was so happy that he was part of the solution!)* Let's make that our secret word.

The essential key is that in the numerous times that I had to use our "secret" word in the future, it was *never* through gritted teeth or with anger or annoyance. It was always with a squeeze of his hand and a loving whisper in his ear: "Inappropriate, sweetie."

Ady's response was always, "*Thank you.*"

This continued for long months—but less and less frequently. Eventually, all off-color behavior completely stopped. In the last few years of Ady's life, I never had to use our secret word again. Once again it reinforced the philosophy that critical words brought opposition, while supportive words brought success. What matters, ultimately, beyond the words themselves, is not just the message but how that message is delivered—with irritation, or with kindness and support.

Periodically I would let Ady know how proud I was of him for stopping the negative behavior. I never took any positive step for granted, always heaping praise on every accomplishment.

I cannot describe what a triumph that was for me. It so strongly reinforced my sense that gentle, kind, supportive, encouraging reactions on my part could actually change unwanted behavior. How powerful is that!

The Positive Effect of Praise and Support

Many Alzheimer's patients, at least in the earlier years, are keenly aware of their own decline. I believe one of their great fears is losing the respect and admiration of their spouse, family, and friends. The more reassurance we can give our loved ones, the more we can allow them to preserve their dignity. The more we treat them with kindness and respect, the less they will tend toward anger.

Ady had another powerful advantage working for him. Though neither of our adult children lived anywhere near us, they had profound appreciation, respect, and love for their father, who was solidly there for them all their lives. Throughout his decline, he was surrounded by their love and he treasured it.

We all thrive on praise, at any age or in any condition. Often the praise is a brief word or two, but the effect is major. I recall Ady's first stage of mobility after hip surgery. He would lean on his walker or cane and shuffle forward, two inches at a time. The physical therapists and I were trying to teach him to lift his knee instead and to put one foot in front of the other. Whenever he managed this, we would cheer him on. "Good job!" At those words his smile would light up his face, and he would try even harder. He no longer thought of himself as a beaten man who could not walk. He began to see himself as one who was conquering his frailty.

This further illuminated an obvious but important principle. Although my praise was a sincere expression of appreciation for an achievement or a behavior, I realized it was also a way of shaping Ady's thinking and attitude, a way of recognizing and acknowledging behavior that I wanted to reinforce.

Praise is only effective if it is real and not simply patronizing. When responding with warmth became a conscious choice, I occasionally wondered if I was responding in an almost manipulative way, just thinking of myself, because Ady responded so positively to kindness and so negatively to confrontation. But I soon learned that I had embarked on a win-win method of keeping each of us happy. Much later, as I understood how profoundly effective this tenderness was, I became proud that I was helping him to live with dignity. I consciously tried to treat my husband with respect and love. The reward was not only his sense of peace, security, and happiness, but that he never moved on to the typical Alzheimer's anger stages. It could have gone in that direction. As I indicated earlier, Ady clearly showed signs of that inclination. By finding ways we could work together, however, we managed to nip in the bud early angry expressions before they became entrenched habits.

Praise and thanks need not be linked to a particular accomplishment. Ady wrote me in his almost nightly notes, "I love you so much. I appreciate all that you are doing for me. I'm so lucky to have you!" My response would be something like: "We're both lucky. You've been there for me all these years and supported me in everything I wanted to do or become. Even now, you show your love for me in so many ways, encouraging me to get out and live, as you always have done." Letting him know that I appreciated his encouragement helped make the effect of his support more tangible for him. He would respond, "I want you to live as fully as you always have." Every time I went out for a tennis game, he would say, "I'm so happy that you're getting to play."

The crucial principle is the supreme value of support and praise. Again, just as it is in raising a child, the value of positive reinforcement is magical. I repeatedly thanked and spelled out which action on his part made my life better or brought me happiness. I believe he was so appreciative of the loving care he received, and so eager to please me, that his positive actions were a reflection of that desire. As a result, I tried to acknowledge every behavior that pointed in a positive direction and never took it for granted.

Under normal circumstances one would not dream of praising a spouse for remembering a name. Living with a husband with Alzheimer's, however, I seized on every small positive act. There were times at a concert, for example, when Ady saw people that we hadn't seen in ages. He would look across the aisle and suddenly say, "There's Brenda and Ralph." For a healthy person, this would have been trivial. For a person in Ady's condition, it was no small achievement, and I never let it pass as something to be expected. Instead I would say, "Good for you! That's amazing. I never would have thought that you knew their names." Ady loved the praise, and he happily kept trying to remember other people's names.

Ady's responses constantly reinforced the analogy I've made to the guidelines for raising children. We don't get angry with a child who is not ready to do algebra. We don't get angry with a toddler who asks "why" in response to virtually every word we say. I consciously chose not to allow myself to show anger towards the man I loved because he could no longer do the things he once did well. This would not have yielded positive results. What worked so successfully for me with Ady were hugs, warmth, and lots of affection and praise.

The Importance of Trust and Truth

In some of the books I've read, the author admits to telling "white lies" to their spouse in an effort to keep them calmer. While I find no fault with anything that works for others, for me that was not an option. I was always direct and honest with Ady, never bending the truth. I believe he instinctively understood this, and it made him far more trusting of decisions I made on his behalf—especially in the later years, when he encouraged me to take over the control of financial affairs.

Even if you have not hitherto had a relationship of trust, it is important to realize that this illness may be an opportunity to start building that trust. Whatever your past relationship may have been, when you truly understand how beneficial it is to both you and your spouse, it's never too late to begin building a relationship of trust—even if it is in the later stage of your marriage. Remember, the praise you give is not just a one-way gift; it makes you a partner in the potential success. The success becomes not only your loved one's but yours to share as a couple or a family.

The Second Spouse

While on the subject of trust, I'd like to offer a few thoughts, though I'm certainly not an authority, on the increasingly common predicament of being the second spouse when your loved one's children by a previous marriage do not trust you. I have had solemn conversations with friends who are experiencing this sad situation. Even in the case of death, rather than divorce, when a second wife has seemingly given her husband happiness and companionship, adult children are often instinctively resentful. It's important to be aware of this common problem and perhaps to seek professional guidance for you or for the family as a whole. Though I don't have all the answers, I do know it's important to try to discuss your concerns with the family from the very first stages of any serious medical issue. Invite them to join you at the doctor's visits. Sometimes, you've run yourself ragged going to many specialists with differing opinions and present the conclusion to the children as a fait accompli. Approaching the children can be harder once medical issues become severe. They may attribute the blackest of intentions to you. Their reaction may be to demand an opinion from a doctor they are more familiar with. They want to be part of the decision, and their mistrust of you may become stronger. They wonder: Are you looking to be free of a sick man? Are you eager to take over the home or apartment?

It's important to build a partnership and trust early on. This may even include enlisting your spouse's help, if he or she is still competent. If your relationship is a good one, it might be helpful if your husband expressed to his adult children how you have enhanced his life and kept him happy. He can become an ally in requesting that his children work with you and respect your role in providing the best care possible. (Of course, the same applies to a remarried husband caring for his second wife, or to a partner caring for a loved one.)

Conclusion

Treating a patient with unconditional love, support, kindness, and patience has at least two potential positive results. First, a happier, more secure and peaceful patient. Life is so much easier living with a happy person than an angry one. Second, emotions like anger, frustration, and insecurity are not constructive. A supportive, calm atmosphere and an active mind are more likely to allow the patient to summon the regenerative power to possibly build new passageways to circumvent the old damaged ones.

Couples who have had a good, solid, wholesome relationship to build on are lucky. But even if one's relationship has not been ideal, the newly dependent relationship that Alzheimer's imposes gives one the chance to make these difficult years better. Your loved one is already feeling severely diminished. Anger on either side is a debilitating and unhealthy emotion. Whatever you can do to build self-esteem with kindness and compassion will make *both* your lives better.

I know the following words are much easier to say than to put into action, but the strongest message I can impart is this simple formula: The more we give kindness, tenderness, appreciation, and respect, the more we will receive those qualities in return. We *can* help to avert the severe decree of Alzheimer's. We do have the potential to make a difference even with the harsh sentence that progressive dementia imposes. We *can* make both our life and our loved one's life more rewarding. Our work as caregivers is not easy, but there are options to help us reap the dividends that we have sowed through many years. If we are successful in making these years a calm and even happy time, it is an extraordinary gift to both our loved one and ourselves.

The following chapter on methodology gives specific examples of how we put these principles into practice.

CHAPTER SEVEN

The Vital Importance of an Active Mind

ADY'S WAS NOT JUST A LIFE OF PASSIVE ACCEPTANCE. In addition to his predictable daily routine, I and those who helped care for him provided almost constant mental stimulation throughout his day. Except during his nap time, his mind was kept challenged—not for an occasional hour or two each day but for virtually every waking moment. Ady continually tried new activities and learned new skills. I used all the creativity and ingenuity I could muster, and I encouraged those helping me to determine what would appeal to him. Not all our ideas worked, but some that didn't work at first succeeded later, as his mind improved. When he was successful, he seemed to relish his accomplishments, and we all viewed his often-unexpected progress with delight.

This chapter discusses some of the activities that engaged him. Your own patient, of course, will be different. You will know best which activities will appeal to them. Trying new options is an adventure for both you and your loved one. Some of the activities

Ady found most engaging and rewarding were ones he had never tried before!

Drawing

One night after dinner I put a stack of blank paper in front of Ady with a beautiful new set of colored pencils, markers, and crayons, and said, "Draw something."

Ady looked at me in shock. He was an engineer, and he drew quite precise floor plans for the homes he built, but I don't think he had ever held a crayon, and he had never been encouraged to draw as a child. (I don't know how he got through kindergarten.)

"What do you want me to draw?"

"Whatever makes you happy!"

So he gave it a try. His first drawings were tentative and primitive. As the months and years went by, they became more detailed. Throughout the years that followed, he almost never left the dinner table without drawing something different and creative. I have stacks of his nightly drawings to this day.

Three aspects of his drawing delighted me. First, he was willing to try an endeavor that was totally new to him. Second, his drawings were full of joy. Even the windows he drew of our home had smiling faces. Finally, he was so proud of his accomplishments that he signed and dated most of his drawings—without any suggestion on my part that he do so. Examples of his drawings appear throughout this book.

WRITING NIGHTLY LETTERS

Perhaps the most extraordinary expression of Ady's well-being, and the one I treasured most, were his almost nightly letters to me.

Ady was never really a writer, and I'm not sure how the nightly letter writing began. I might have been out at theater and came home to find a letter to me on the table near the front door. Whatever the circumstances of the first letter, I was overjoyed, and I

JULY 15, 2010

DEAR HELENE,

YOU WERE 19 WHEN I MET YOU,

AND 19 WHEN I MARRIED YOU!

AND YOUR MOTHER TOOK A LIKING TO ME FROM THE 1ST DAY! SHE HAD GOOD VISION!

I LOVE YOU, SO!

Ady

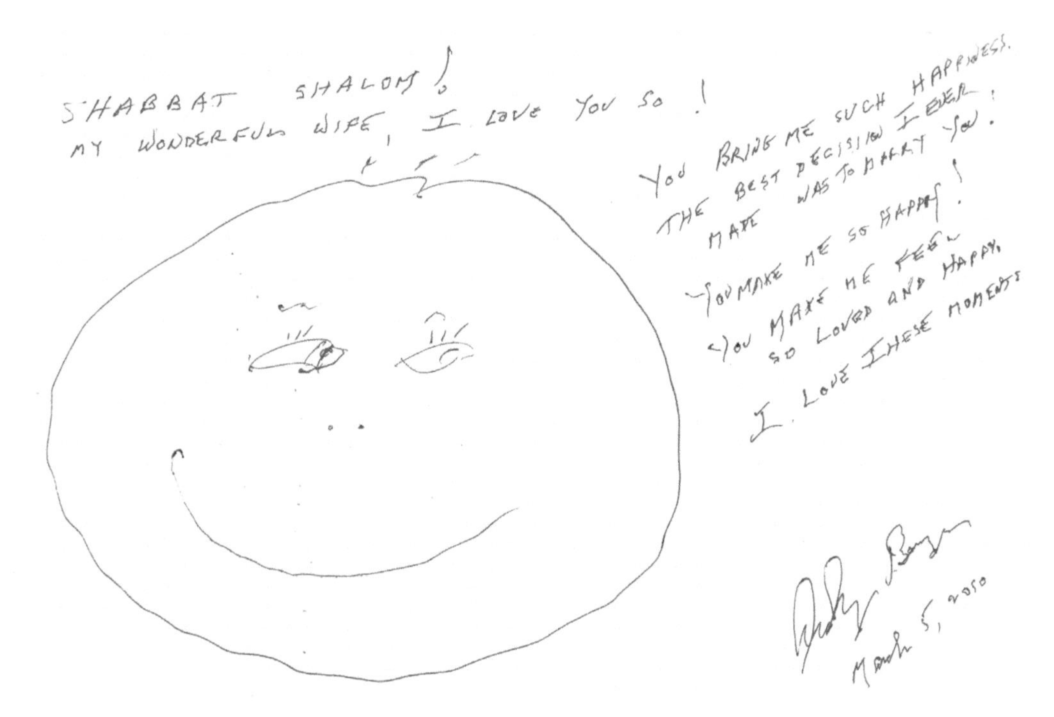
SHABBAT SHALOM!
MY WONDERFUL WIFE, I LOVE YOU SO!
YOU BRING ME SUCH HAPPINESS.
THE BEST DECISION I EVER MADE WAS TO MARRY YOU.
YOU MAKE ME SO HAPPY!
YOU MAKE ME FEEL SO LOVED AND HAPPY.
I LOVE THESE MOMENTS
March 5, 2020

communicated that pleasure to him. Once he had started, Ady continued to write his brief "love letters" almost nightly, even if I was at my desk in the next room.

Ady's letters (and his whimsical drawings) were a clear window to his state of mind. The letters expressed happiness, appreciation, and contentment. They showed astounding awareness and were powerful statements of love. In the years since he's been gone, when I sometimes wonder if I'm embellishing the happiness he expressed, I look at these letters and drawings and see documentation of my memory.

Neither the letters nor the drawings would have been possible in the first few years after the diagnosis. During those early years, he did not have the capacity to verbalize his feelings. As his sense of peace and joy was rekindled, the expression of it came through in his writings. I perceived them as a testament to both his state of mind and the regeneration of his brain.

Answering Written Questions

One of the many creative innovations Lizette introduced was to give Ady a page of written questions, leaving blank space in between for him to respond in his own hand. She did this almost nightly, after dinner. I'm not sure how it began. I think I went to my desk for a short while and when I returned I found Ady proudly holding up the paper with his answers. Lizette's English then was nowhere near what it became, but that did not matter. Her questions were remarkably varied: about family, his youth, what he enjoyed, about me or how we met, politics, future events, current events, music, recent performances, and much more. The sample letters included here (pp. 98–100) were all written in Ady's final year, the sixth year of his diagnosed Alzheimer's. Selected from hundreds of others, they show his degree of cognition, ability to recall information, and feelings of contentment and peace.

Playing Challenging Games

Alzheimer's patients will not retain their former prowess with games, and a little adaptation may be necessary. Even with reduced ability, however, there are many benefits to playing challenging games.

Sudoku

About two years after his diagnosis, I tried to introduce Ady to Sudoku. Since he had such skill and fascination with math and numbers, I assumed he would enjoy Sudoku and be quite good at it.

I was wrong. He had no interest in it. He couldn't understand the point of putting all the numbers into those little boxes. It was a frustrating experience for him.

After another year of constant mental stimulation, I reintroduced Sudoku. To my amazement, he not only was able to grasp

Which is you favorite time wish your wife?

DANCING WITH HER IN MY ARMS.

What is your planning for this Summer?

TO GO TO THE BERKSHIRES WITH HELENE.

Tell me about Israel?

IT IS A BEAUTIFUL COUNTRY WHERE THE PEOPLE ARE FREE TO DO WHAT THEY WANT.

What Do you like must about your Wife?

HELENE IS LOVING AND CARING AND WONDERFUL, AND I LOVE EVERYTHING ABOUT HER.

[signature]
March 9, 2010

What political paties do you have in US.

DEMOCRATS
REPUBLICANS
INDEPENDENTS

Whath is the more problem now Haiti?

PEOPLE ARE HUNGRY
AFTER THE EARTH QUAKE.

Whath is the more problem important for el president USA.

UNEMPLOYMENT

Where is the city the White House?

WASHINGTON, D.C

Tell me about you?

I STARTED OUT BY BUILDING HOUSES IN PEMBROKE PINES.
WE USED SOLID POURED CONCRETE GARAGES.

when is your beutiful experience which your wife?

WHEN I MET HELÈNE, SHE WAS ONLY 19 YEARS OLD, STANDING BY THE SIDE OF THE POOL IN A BATHING SUIT! AND I FELL IN LOVE IMMEDIATELY. WE GOT MARRIED 9 MONTHS LATER, WHEN SHE WAS STILL 19!

When is your best time which you son mark. years ago?

MY SON, MARK, AND I TOOK A BICYCLE TRIP THRU IRELAND, AND IT WAS WONDERFUL.

when is your best time which you Daughter Bonie. Few years ago?

I LOVE TO SWIM LAPS WITH BONNIE— SHE IS REALLY, REALLY GOOD!

for why you are very Happy?

I LOVE MY WIFE AND SHE LOVES ME!

TUESDAY APRIL 20, 2010
ABY BERGER

the concept but was able to complete most of the puzzles. It became another thing we did together: I had never played Sudoku before and enjoyed sitting with Ady and watching him develop this new skill. Sometimes he got tired and we stretched a puzzle over two nights, but I never gave hints or suggestions. He expressed such pleasure from each number that he got right, looking up at me with a glorious grin and loving the praise he got from me for every correct addition.

This new ability, perhaps more dramatically than any others, convinced me that all the constant stimulation was having a powerful effect. New brain connections were surely being made.

Chess

As a young man, Ady was an excellent chess player, acquiring many master points. He once was one of fifty simultaneous players against Grandmaster Samuel Reshevsky. Reshevsky beat them all, one by one, and Ady was the last one still alive. Ady said that he resigned very quickly because the pressure was too great, and he felt his moves were taking too long, but that accomplishment was a source of pride for years thereafter. In the early years of our marriage he had gone occasionally to the little outdoor Miami Beach Chess Club to play with "the old men" at the club.

I tried to encourage him to play chess again after his diagnosis, but it was hard to find partners. When Ady did occasionally find a player, he still had the ability to think ahead, plan his moves—and take the person he was playing into account. I knew how the pieces moved and the essential play of the game, but I never really had a head for chess. In the last few years, when Ady occasionally asked me to play after dinner, he became the tutor. He had always been an excellent teacher, and he felt empowered by the opportunity our games gave him to teach. We both genuinely enjoyed those evenings together.

When our grandchildren visited during the Alzheimer's years, our grandson, Alex, was then about eleven and on the chess team at school. Ady invited Alex to play. Ady offered him a draw in the first game and won the second. He then asked our granddaughter, Rachel, age 8½, to play. She "won" her game, which made her very happy, though later she was wise enough to say, "Grandpa let me win!" This, too, was typical of Ady. He felt a boy Alex's age could handle the loss but didn't want to discourage his younger granddaughter. About four years into Alzheimer's, Ady clearly still retained some of his emotional intelligence.

Computer Games

Based on the numerous articles recommending computer games as an excellent stimulus for the brain, I tried exposing Ady to them several times. He was clearly not interested. His embrace of Sudoku (an entirely new concept) and chess (an old skill) when I reintroduced them several years later may have had something to do with my being totally present for these two activities, whereas the computer was a lonely exercise. I suspect others might have more success with computer games. It is definitely worth introducing them.

Reviving a Musical Instrument

The most exciting venture was the revival of Ady's wonderful ability at the piano—an ability that had lain dormant for several years.

"I miss your piano playing," I told him one day. "Why did you stop?"

"I can't play anymore."

"Why?"

"Because my fingers don't work anymore."

"Maybe your fingers don't work because you've stopped playing.

You used to get such pleasure at the piano. Will you try giving it ten minutes a day and see if your strength comes back?"

And so it began. Ady started slowly at first, playing for just the ten minutes he had promised. But sometimes abilities or interests one was exposed to as a child can trigger positive memories and reinforce old abilities. For the next three years, Ady played every day, finally building up to at least an hour of daily satisfaction and pleasure. He played from the repertoire he had learned as a young boy—which, fortunately, was a large one. He played Mozart, Beethoven, Rachmaninoff, Brahms, and more. In the past, he had known these pieces by heart. Now he needed the score. Far from regarding this as a regression, I saw this as an advantage, adding visual decoding to the combination of finger agility and muscle memory that relearning every piece required.

I do not have the words to describe the pleasure Ady received from his daily time at the piano—or the pleasure he gave all of us

THE FIRST TIME I PLAYED THE PIANO,
SINCE I WAS 10 YEARS OLD, IT WAS IN
1940. AND I USED TO PRACTICE EVERY
DAY, AND I STILL DO. AND I FIND IT VERY
RELAXING.
I PLAY BEETHOVEN AND MOZART, AND
RUSSIAN CHOPSTICKS,
AND END UP WITH THE UKELELE!

[illegible]
SEPT 14, 2010

who heard him. He had never been shy about playing for others. For years when he knew guests were to arrive at our home, he always got ready early and wanted to be at the piano when they arrived. He was so proud! Once he started playing the piano again, he also renewed his love of playing the ukulele.

If your loved one played an instrument, their engagement with that instrument has the potential to be a significant part of their therapy. Music had always been an important part of Ady's life, but I could never have dreamt what a magical part of his therapy it would become. *In his last few months, Ady actually began to tackle new pieces.*

My observations of the impact of music on Ady's mind, spirit, and sense of well-being are supported by the findings reported in the movie *Alive Inside,* which I described in chapter 6.

The Importance of Limiting Television Time

Most of the solutions to the problems we encountered were not obvious in the beginning. They took trial and error and sometimes intense arguments until they were worked out satisfactorily for each of us.

Television was an especially touchy subject. One of the issues Ady and I disagreed on most fiercely was when Ady, abetted by an inadequate aide, became too dependent on television. (I have related in chapter 6 the resistance he had to having his bathroom TV taken away.) The last thing I wanted was to see my husband become a blank-faced zombie in front of the TV. We worked to find creative ways to give Ady nearly constant mental stimulation during most of his waking hours. After dinner, however, when either drawing or Sudoku were completed, he was ready for the pure relaxation of television for a limited time—usually about forty-five minutes—and with carefully chosen programs.

During an earlier period, he was fascinated by the series *24*, where each episode covers twenty-four hours in the life of a counterterrorism agent. The timing was perfect, because each episode, without commercials, lasted about forty-five minutes. Later, when the installments grew too violent for him or the plot intrigues became too difficult to follow, watching the program created too much tension. I observed that he became agitated rather than relaxed by either the violence or his awareness that he was not following the plot. We began to have him select from classic favorites like *Casablanca* or musicals he was familiar with, so that he could often sing along. I don't believe he was even aware of the shift in programming, but he appeared more relaxed and smiling when we turned the movie off, even if it was to be continued the next evening.

As I have related in chapter 6, in the process of changing what Ady watched, we followed the important principle of asking rather than telling: "Which of these movies would you like to watch tonight?" rather than "Here's the movie we're going to watch tonight." The more we offered choice rather than direction, the more Ady had the feeling of empowerment. When we realized how successful this approach was, we began to put virtually every decision or direction in the form of a question. The choices were always options we thought were appropriate and healthy. The more we continued to give Ady choices in all areas, the more he felt empowered. Rather than being told what to do, this seemingly simple shift in approach gave him a sense of dignity and control.

Regular Outings

Many Alzheimer's patients may enjoy not only making art but being an audience as well. Even if you cannot awaken their inclination to create, the benefits of appropriate outings can have an impact.

As Ady's disease progressed, our social life became increasingly restricted. Ady was unable to engage for long periods of time, and I did not want to burden all but our closest friends for an entire evening. But we continued to attend as many as two or three concerts a week, and these outings became a large part of Ady's social world.

Ady had a profound love and understanding of classical music and opera. After his hip surgery, we would always arrive early, so I could get him out of the wheelchair and transferred to his seat. Because of the wheelchair, we were usually given aisle seats, and Ady would hold court as everyone he knew in the audience would stop by to say hello. Ady often addressed them by name. The benefits to his mind and spirits were palpable.

We were fortunate that Ady never spoke or made noise during the actual performance. I could not have continued to take him if he disrupted a concert in any way, but I never sat in fear that he would call attention to himself or behave inappropriately. (Whether your loved one is capable of this is a matter for each caregiver to decide.) In Ady's last two years, we reached a point where attendance past intermission was too exhausting for him. This did not necessarily manifest at the concert itself, but afterwards. After he came home it took Ady at least two hours to complete all his medical treatments and get ready for bed. It also caused havoc the following day if he did not get enough sleep with his demanding schedule.

Usually, I left the concert with him, but if it was a work I particularly wanted to hear, I would get an extra ticket for his favorite aide, Lizette, so she could come with us for the first half and take him home at intermission. She became a lover of classical music, both because of what played daily in his bathroom and her attendance with us at the concerts.

Your loved one's interests may be entirely different—perhaps

FEB 2010

DEAR RACHEL!
I WOULD LIKE TO WISH YOU A
HAPPY BIRTHDAY! I LOVE LISTENING
TO YOU PLAYING THE PIANO. AND I
UNDERSTAND YOU ARE PLAYING TENNIS SO WELL TOO.
I AM SO PROUD OF YOU.

LOVE, KISSES, AND HUGS,
GRANDPA

fishing on a pier, or a football, basketball, or baseball game. Whatever gave him or her pleasure in the past, even though the outings take effort, try to recapture those times of pleasure.

Calls with Friends

One major plus for Ady's spirits and cognitive functioning were the almost daily telephone calls from friends. They were not long or involved, just a simple touching base to find out how he was. One friend, Kenny Schwartz, called Ady every day for at least ten years, seldom missing a day. Their calls were brief. "How many laps did you swim today? How far did you walk?" (Sometimes I think

Ady pushed to do more exercise because he knew Kenny would ask him later what he had accomplished.) Friends like Kenny are rare, but others called regularly as well.

There were also many calls that Ady initiated himself. Much of the credit for this was due to Kenny's wife, Maxine, who years before gave Ady a small calendar to be used solely for the purpose of recording birthdays, anniversaries, and other important events. Ady used his "birthday book" for the next forty years to call hundreds of people on their birthdays and anniversaries.

I often wondered if our friends found this touching or annoying, especially in later years, when Ady still called to wish a happy anniversary to a friend who had lost their spouse. I tried crossing out those events in Ady's book with a big black line, but he ignored the lines and called anyway. Apparently, my concern was misplaced. Long after Ady's passing, I still got calls from people who call me on *their* birthdays to tell me how much they miss Ady's calls. I don't think Ady ever felt cut off from the world.

Results and Conclusions

Ady's nightly letters were a wonderful expression of his sense of appreciation, accomplishment, and contentment. He relished each achievement. He felt empowered rather than diminished, proud rather than disappointed. Day after day, he experienced successes rather than failures. His letters and whimsical drawings were a clear window to his state of mind, which I believe helped to make his regeneration possible.

On the day of Ady's diagnosis, I vowed to try to keep sweetness and joy in our lives. I never could have anticipated how rich that joy would be. Nor could I have known that my joy would emanate from the sense of achievement in witnessing Ady's progress, and the satisfaction of knowing that the care I gave him was partly responsible for it. But these years were not a one-way street, with all the giving on my part. Ady sustained me, as well, with so much expressed appreciation and love.

It's a different kind of love, to be sure. The feelings one gets in caring for an adult parent or spouse are a little bit like the feelings one gets from giving constant care to a baby. The person you're caring for has no understanding of a movie plot, or a book, or a piece of news on the radio. You don't get back an intellectual discussion. But that baby's smile is your reward, and it is enough. Though he read the newspaper every day, Ady couldn't discuss the article he just finished reading, or even remember its content—but he seemed to remember everything that was truly important in our lives. The joy I received in our last years together was rooted in an appreciation of our past, of what we shared, of the children we raised together, and of what we gave together to our community. This was my time to express my appreciation for the lifetime of emotional, financial, and physical support that Ady gave to me. I felt blessed to be able to give back to him, and to have him know what he meant to me.

Ady's sense of accomplishment was borne out by medical observation. As part of his regular checkups, Ady routinely went through a battery of tests at the Wien Center. Dr. Duara was constantly surprised at the excellent results as compared to the physical damage he saw on the brain scans. During one visit, I heard him say aside to a doctor in training, "There's a lot of residual there," referring to the brain capacity Ady had left. As he continued to improve, I became more convinced that what the testing scores showed was more than just "residual"—that the constant mental stimulation and his calm surroundings were helping his brain create new passages around the damaged ones. In his last year, as he continued to do what he could not do before, I began to believe Dr. Duara's assurance that regeneration was possible.

CHAPTER EIGHT

Create a Healthy and Safe Environment

VIRTUALLY EVERY ARTICLE WE READ ON THE SUBJECT of Alzheimer's includes sections on exercise, healthy eating, and getting enough sleep. The goal of this chapter is to encourage you to devote renewed attention to these life basics.

EXERCISE

Look around you at people in their seventies or eighties who do not have Alzheimer's. I think you'll observe, as I have, that those who have not adopted some regular regimen of exercise, even a daily walk, appear far less likely to be in good health. The mind is often not as sharp. Their posture is less likely to be erect. Their walk is slow and tentative. These observations are more marked in people with Alzheimer's or dementia. But the fact that a person's mind is deteriorating does not necessarily mean that their bodies have to stop functioning fully as well. To remain healthy, our bodies need exercise.

The links between physical exercise, health, mental learning, and clarity are now well established. Exercise is certainly not a guarantee of health, but *not* exercising may be a guarantee of *lack* of health. We may not be able to stop the mind from deteriorating, but we can encourage the movement that will keep the body fit. "Exercise may help to keep the brain robust in people who have an increased risk of developing Alzheimer's disease, according to an inspiring new study," a *New York Times* blog reported. "The findings suggest that even moderate amounts of physical activity may help to slow the progression of one of the most dreaded diseases of aging."* An article from the Mayo clinic supports this conclusion: "Studies show that people who are physically active are less likely to experience a decline in their mental function and have a lowered risk of developing Alzheimer's disease."†

The question is, how can we encourage those we care for who are *not* in the habit of exercising (even if it's only a mild walk three or more times a week) to begin to move? Our experience suggests a couple of general principles.

Explain the Benefits

Most people are frightened when they sense their minds slipping or receive an Alzheimer's diagnosis. If we can help them to understand that moving the body can be of help in fighting the disease, they may be more open to suggestions and willing to try an approach they may not have considered before.

---

* Gretchen Reynolds, "Can Exercise Reduce Alzheimer's Risk?" *New York Times,* Well, July 2, 2014. https://well.blogs.nytimes.com/2014/07/02/can-exercise-reduce-alzheimers-risk/.

† Ronald Petersen, M.D., "Can exercise prevent memory loss and improve cognitive function?" Mayoclinic.org, October 22, 2014. https://www.mayoclinic.org/diseases-conditions/alzheimers-disease/expert-answers/alzheimers-disease/faq-20057881.

With that goal clear in your mind, it might be helpful to sit down and attempt to have a rational conversation explaining the potential benefits of daily exercise. It's clearly difficult at this stage to encourage new behavior. Yet the patient might embrace the idea of a nonmedical or surgical way to make a difference, if the benefits are rationally and lovingly explained.

Meet Them Where They Are

If mental or physical limitations preclude certain forms of physical activity, one can try to find activities in which your loved one *can* engage. Look for opportunities to turn a negative situation into a positive one: the need to stop driving, for example, might encourage more walking to nearby destinations.

Ady's asthma kept him from more rigorous exercise like jogging or competitive sports, so we encouraged swimming, walking, and biking (in the early stages). We tried to capitalize on existing interests. Ady's interest in swimming dated back to his time on the freshman team at Dartmouth, and he taught our children to swim at a very young age. In the early years of his Alzheimer's we encouraged him to take almost daily swims. He had to give up biking during the Alzheimer's years when we realized that it was no longer safe, but we then purchased a stationary bike, which was less pleasurable but physically of equal value. Ady used that bike watching TV almost daily. *Be creative. Make it fun—join in.*

After Ady's hip fracture, two and a half years before he passed away, he did physical therapy at home five days a week with a trainer, as prescribed by his doctor and covered by insurance. When that ended he continued the daily workouts as a fitness program. While that might be unaffordable for some, there are many fitness or rehab programs connected to hospitals, community centers, and doctors' offices that are more affordable. Check out programs in your area.

The discipline of having to be at a certain place at a certain time, instead of doing it when the whim strikes, is more likely to be effective. The choice of "whether" is no longer on the table. It's part of the daily schedule and no longer up for discussion.

Diet

There are hundreds, probably thousands of books on healthy eating. I don't intend to add to the literature. The point I do want to make is the increasingly emphasized connection between slowing Alzheimer's symptoms and being aware of what we put into our bodies each day. WebMD reports: "Researchers have found that people who stuck to a diet that included foods like berries, leafy greens, and fish had a major drop in their risk for [Alzheimer's]."* It is never too late to begin a healthy diet.

Many of the same principles of motivation discussed in relation to the need to be physically fit also apply to convincing your loved one of the need for a healthy diet—even if he or she has been a lifelong pizza and soda lover:

- Explain the reasons for the diet adjustment.
- Join your loved one in eating in a healthier way.
- Serve only food that is healthy and avoid bringing food that is not into your home.
- Substitute roasted unsalted nuts for salty chips.
- Try interesting and hearty soups with lots of vegetables.
- Offer appetizing, healthy choices and serve them attractively.
- Be creative, and the patient may not even notice that the diet has changed.

* Camille Noe Pagán, "The MIND Diet May Help Prevent Alzheimer's," webmd.com, https://www.webmd.com/alzheimers/features/mind-diet-alzheimers-disease#1.

Many people enjoy variety. Ady was not one of those. Much to my amazement, he was never bored with the same regimen of food every day. It was hard to be creative because he did not want variety. For example, here's his "daily breakfast" menu—and I mean daily; he never wavered. The aides that we had during his final two years used this as their daily guide.

Daily Breakfast Menu (same every day)

- Whole orange cut in eighths
- Two hard-boiled eggs (whites only)
- Cold cereal with skim milk (Raisin Bran, Special K, or Corn Flakes)
- With whole sliced banana
- Yogurt (fruit or plain) with low-salt cottage cheese and fresh fruit (usually berries)

On the rare occasion that we were invited to a brunch, Ady had his breakfast at home. I suspect that many patients would be more comfortable with the food they are used to at home.

Sleep

The Alzheimer's and Dementia Caregiver's Center acknowledges the connection between Alzheimer's and sleep: "People with Alzheimer's and dementia may have problems sleeping or increases in behavioral problems that begin at dusk and last into the night (known as sundowning)."* Their literature offers both causes and coping strategies. Among the causes they discuss are exhaustion, sensing and reacting to their caregiver's frustration, and general

* This and subsequent material (causes and coping strategies) from "Sleep Issues and Sundowning," Alzheimer's and Dementia Caregiver Center, www.alz.org.

disorientation. Among the coping strategies are assuring a safe and comfortable sleep environment, avoiding stimulants, and keeping the patient actively involved during the day.

We were extremely lucky in that sleep was not a problem for us. Ady slept well, eight to nine and a half hours a night, even after taking the forty-five-minute nap that he seemed to require every day.

I attribute, in part, Ady's ability to sleep to his upbeat mood when he was awake and to the calm, peaceful, and ordered schedule of his day. He went to sleep untroubled, knowing that we were there for him and that he was still respected and appreciated. He knew what to expect and when. There was no uncertainty in his life.

Towards the end of this chapter in the "Safety" section, one of the essentials I list is a digital clock with large, well-lit, easily readable numbers. This was a reassuring item for Ady. When he glanced up at night, he could read the time and know if it was the middle of the night or almost time to get up. It kept him from being disoriented. The next chapter discusses the importance of a schedule that is reliable and understood.

Another important and often-overlooked subject that the Alzheimer's Center advises is: *Be mindful of your* own *mental and physical exhaustion.* If you are feeling stressed by the late afternoon, the patient may pick up on it and become agitated or confused. Try to get plenty of rest at night so you have more energy during the day.

I discuss this more fully in chapter 12 (Giving Yourself What You Need), but the point here is that your mood and attitude have a direct effect on the patient's well-being. Always be aware that, while your patient's memory may be deficient, there is a heightened sensitivity to your mood, tension, and frustration. None of us sleeps well on the nights when we have extra tension, are frustrated, angry, or have unresolved issues.

Dealing with Incontinence

People suffering from Alzheimer's and dementia frequently develop incontinence at some stage of the disease. Various steps and strategies can be helpful for patients who are cooperative and awake (see the section on incontinence on the website of the Alzheimer's Association or comparable organizations), but the problem becomes more difficult at night. Finding HDIS (Home Delivery Incontinence Supplies), a company that specializes in incontinence products delivered directly to your home, was of incalculable help to us, as they carried so many products that standard drugstores do not offer.

They were also extremely helpful on the phone with guidance. Before I spoke to them, for example, I was putting a "guard" inside Ady's nighttime diaper, mistakenly thinking that would help him get through the night more comfortably. They explained that since the guards I was using had a waterproof liner, what I was doing was trapping the moisture in and not letting it pass through to the more absorbent diaper. They had a product that was exactly what I was looking for but did not know existed: a guard without the waterproof liner that provided another layer of absorbency to carry urine away from the body. Once I began using these guards, Ady almost never experienced the leakage that we used to have before. Instead, he—and I!—were able to sleep uninterrupted through the night, a major gift.

There are dozens of other places to find incontinence products, including local drugstores and a host of other medical supply stores and online sites, like:

- North Shore care supply
- Cheap Chux
- Incontinence Shop

Your own research will surely come up with additional names.

SAFETY: BATHROOM MODIFICATIONS

Older sufferers from Alzheimer's and dementia frequently suffer from other problems as well, and Ady was no exception. After Ady fractured his hip, two and a half years before he died, the bathroom became a much more hazardous place. We are lucky to have so many marvelous products out there to solve such problems. Every one of the following bathroom modifications was so simple and so obvious. To the novice that I was, however, it took a while to figure out each one, so I offer them here in the hope that you can get your loved one the degree of comfort and safety he or she needs as soon as possible.

I would recommend going—in person, if possible—to a good store that specializes in medical equipment and looking around to see what products exist. I was amazed by what's available. The products provide a safer environment even for those who are *not* injured. For one with diminished awareness because of Alzheimer's, these tools are essential.

Wet Walker for Shower

In addition to the walker on wheels that Ady used to navigate around the house and to take his walks, we had an additional walker in the shower that I called the "wet walker." I took the wheels off and substituted the option of rubber bottoms on the legs. The walker remained in the shower because the tubing would fill up with water. This was such an excellent solution, because it gave Ady independence to be able to handle his shower by himself (with me or an aide close by). Ady was then able to clean his private parts without relying on someone else to do it properly. Maneuvering was vastly easier for him than with the typical shower seat, especially since he was not able to stand up from a shower seat, which usually comes without the side rails he needed in order to stand.

Grab Rails and Mats in Shower

We added two long vertical grab rails in the shower, one next to the entry and one closest to the controls. Ady depended on the greater sense of security that the rails provided. We also added several of those bath mats with rubber suction cups, so the shower floor was not slippery.

Padding on Walker Handles

When I observed Ady's hands getting sore from use of his walker, the simple solution was to add foam or rubber padding to the handrails that I secured with either cloth tape (so the handles were not slippery) or with cling rolls—three-inch, wraparound, self-sticking, stretchable beige bandage tape—so they could be changed easily as needed.

Comfortable Chair in Bathroom

Ady spent a great deal of time in his bathroom each day with his many treatments—more hours than he could remain standing. He also needed to sit for his vest treatments and to put on his support hose. I bought a really comfortable light chair *with* arms that could be moved around easily. He depended on the arms to be able to get up and down.

Raised Toilet Seat with Arms

Ady's hip fracture made it extremely difficult for him to get up from a toilet seat. The whole world probably knows about raised toilet seats, but I didn't. I was delighted to see many options for raised toilet seats on one of my trips to a quality medical supply store, and I selected one with side rails so he could stand without assistance.

Even with the raised toilet seat with arms, I would consider adding a small grab rail near the toilet on whatever adjacent wall or cabinet is solid.

Safety: Comfort Outside the Bathroom

Wheelchair with Large Rear Wheels

My first wheelchair was a mistake. I purchased the lightest one I could find, which had eight-inch wheels front and back. It was adequate indoors but very difficult on almost any irregular surface outside and totally impossible on grass. After a short period of frustration, I switched to a slightly heavier but still lightweight wheelchair with twelve-inch back wheels. It was still light enough for me to be able to lift into the car trunk when necessary, and it was functional outdoors.

Remove Small Rugs

Small area rugs, even with nonslip padding, are a hazard. I removed them after the first stumble.

Clock with Clearly Visible Numbers

Ady depended on a clock at night to give him the security of knowing the time whenever he awoke, instead of being disoriented and wondering. A digital clock with five-inch tall numerals that were illuminated at night did the trick. You'll find dozens of such clocks with large numbers on the internet.

Wear Comfortable Clothes

Ady always dressed appropriately when out. At home, while walking, or with his trainer, however, we encouraged the easiest and most comfortable clothes possible, usually sweatpants and a T-shirt.

Conclusion

Those who suffer from Alzheimer's and dementia, like other elderly or otherwise handicapped individuals, begin to find even routine daily tasks—walking around in the house, going to the bathroom, and showering—to be increasingly difficult and even dangerous. Fortunately, we live in a time when a range of products and information is available on the internet or in specialty stores.

Finding and installing the right equipment can be time-consuming and complicated, but once you've completed the task, the degree of comfort both you and your patient will feel is worth any amount of effort that goes into making the changes. There is also a psychological adjustment. I remember the momentary pang I felt after the first slight stumble on the pretty oriental rug at the entrance to our bedroom. I knew then that all those small rugs would have to be removed. Seeing my world slowly changing brought on a brief moment of sadness. Be prepared for many such moments, as adjustments in your home will have to be made. But the relief that comes with providing a safe environment promptly puts those minor adjustments into perspective.

PART THREE

INTERACTION WITH OTHERS

HOUSE
MAY 18, 2010

CHAPTER NINE

Aides

FOR THE FIRST THREE AND A HALF YEARS AFTER ADY'S diagnosis, I chose not to have any additional help. Much of my own learning process took place during those years. When Ady returned home after hip surgery from a fall in the bathroom (a procedure that required a week in the hospital and three weeks in rehab), I had no choice. He was wheelchair bound and unable to stand or transfer without help.

The first two weeks home from the hospital, I had aides around the clock, because I needed the help at night. After two weeks at home I reduced the aides' daily schedule, having them come in from breakfast to bedtime. I was very eager to return to my bed and be next to Ady during the night.

The wonder is that after three and a half years of handling all of Ady's care on my own, *I did not understand how much I needed the extra help until I had it.* I was blessed to be able to maintain the aides until Ady passed away.

Life became so much easier for me. It was also the time in which Ady made the greatest mental strides. I was able to give more fully of myself because I was not burned out. I took daily breaks, mostly for exercise or an occasional cultural event or to be with friends. I would come home refreshed and able to give my all to Ady—something that is very difficult, perhaps impossible, to do 24-7 without visible impatience or frustration creeping in.

I urge anyone caring for an Alzheimer's patient to get extra coverage at least a few hours a day. I was fortunate to be able to afford it; I know not everyone can. But one can still reach out to family or close friends, someone who can give you the break that is so essential for your own mental and physical health. Whatever else you have to give up, give yourself the respite you need—even if it's just a long walk by yourself.

Finding the Right Aides

Just having another person does not automatically make your life easier. The person you select must be responsive, caring, and willing to accept direction from you. For me, by far the most challenging part of Ady's care during the latter years was not Ady or the work itself; it was finding and training competent and caring aides to help accomplish what I sought for him. That became a parallel full-time job. Over the next two and a half years we had some extraordinarily wonderful people and some disastrous ones. We had a constantly revolving door, as I learned to quickly let go of those who did not challenge Ady mentally or treat him with the kindness, gentleness, and dignity that I felt he deserved.

The following is what I learned in hiring and managing competent aides and making them engaged partners with me in Ady's care.

My experience was that word of mouth was most likely to ensure a safe and successful outcome. I made numerous calls to friends who had engaged someone for a parent or spouse. Since I did not have a large network of friends who had employed aides,

I found I often relied on a competent aide to recommend others with whom she had shared a case. When that was successful, it worked particularly well because they could cover for each other and depend on one another. But word of mouth was certainly not foolproof. Sometimes an aide would recommend a friend who did not meet the standards that I wanted for Ady, which made it all the more awkward to let her go. But I had only one litmus test: What was best for Ady?

The selection of someone to help after emergency surgery, on the other hand, unless you already have the right person in mind, is usually straightforward. The hospital can give you an agency name, and you take whomever they send. I had 50 percent success. Of the night and day people they sent for twelve-hour shifts, one was competent, the other disinterested and only there for her paycheck.

The Interview: What to Look For

The most essential guidance is to TRUST YOUR INSTINCTS. As Malcolm Gladwell wrote in his book *Blink*, your first impression will tell you much of what you need to know and what to watch for.

Look for a caring and compassionate person. During the interview, watch to see if all the focus is on you. Are they trying to impress you, or trying to engage the patient? Closely observe how they speak to the one they will be caring for. Do they initiate talking to the patient, or only speak to him or her at your direction? Some may put on a phony show of kindness and interest in your presence, but with time and attention, you will learn to recognize if it's artificial or real. Some prospective aides virtually ignored me during the interview and involved Ady immediately. Invariably, those were the ones I selected and who turned out to be the best.

Questions to Cover During the Interview

- Ask for credentials and check them.
- Ask what training they had to become an aide.
- Ask what their last position was and how long they stayed.
- Ask why they left their last position.
- In today's world you also need to inquire about their legal status and receive documentation before you hire.
- Do they have a car, or can they get to your home reliably on public transportation? Occasionally I was impressed with a potential aide, only to find out that a friend drove them to the interview and they had no way of getting to the job.

If someone looks promising, discuss hours and what you're willing to pay. Sometimes, before the issue of salary arose, the candidate would tell me what they get an hour. Often it was consistent with what I'd expect. Occasionally it was a sum that I could not consider.

It is important to look for someone who seems like a good fit both for your spouse and for you! Remember, this person will become an intimate part of your household, knowing not only where you keep his underwear and medication, but, if you're open, as I tended to be, knowing more about you than some of your closest friends. If caution flags go up during the interview, heed them. There were times in the early stages when I had little idea what to look for. I made mistakes that made me feel desperate, thinking that there was absolutely no one out there who had the qualities I was seeking.

Don't despair. There are many fine people who need work. Be creative in your search. Remember that a kind and caring heart, and the desire and ability to learn, can be vastly more important than a piece of paper saying that one has passed certain tests.

Caring aides may be hard to find, but there are lots of really good people out there. You are not seeking a trained, registered nurse who must have a nursing background for someone who is critically ill or recuperating. You are looking for a kind, generally cheerful person willing to engage your patient and to take directions from you. I often found the best people via a nontraditional route, as I relate below with regard to Lizette.

Be Clear About What the Job Entails

In addition to salary and hours, it's important to discuss the expectations of the job, so there are no surprises later. Your expectations regarding food are one example. Some will expect the aide to bring their own lunch. Since my help was on basically a twelve-hour shift (I did not have help at night), I offered the same food we were eating. Occasionally, an aide chose to bring her own sandwich for one of the meals.

One day I happened to walk into the kitchen when one early aide was packing two-thirds of a chicken to take home to her family. When I tried to explain that I was happy to provide food when she was in our home but not for her to take with her, she let out a tirade of wrath towards me. I didn't have to let her go, because it was clear that she was not returning. I paid what I owed, and she left in a huff.

I also explained to all those I interviewed that Lizette was the head caregiver. Because of Ady's complex medications and treatments, she would be training everyone that worked for us for two days before they were on their own. I needed to be certain in advance that they were comfortable with that arrangement and would not resist Lizette's guidance. Every one of the aides appreciated Lizette's gentle guidance and expressed that they would not have known what to do without her.

You will have requirements of your own to be clear about in advance. Whatever they are, it is best to put them out there upfront, or you will go through the complicated days of training only to have them leave.

Don't Let the Aide Intimidate You

Here's a personal story that best illustrates an aide assuming power that was not hers to assume. And I let her!

. . .

When Ady was fifty-eight he had a severe bicycle accident that required hip surgery. About ten days after he returned home, with nurses round the clock, he had to be rushed to the hospital emergency room for what turned out to be a life-threatening phlebitis (inflammation of a vein) in the groin. I waited in the emergency room with one of the aides that had been helping to care for Ady since he had returned from his surgery. When they called Ady in, the aide turned to me and said, in authoritative tones, "Only one person is allowed inside. You'll have to wait out here." Like an obedient child, I listened to her. Later I was furious at myself for not speaking up and saying, "If only one of us goes in, it will be me. *You* wait out here."

It turned out that this aide, who appeared very competent, tried to take over everything and was actively flirting with my husband (who was then fit and good-looking, in his prime, and living in a lovely home). She looked at me with annoyance every time I entered the room. When our son arrived a week later and saw her in action for about an hour, he said, "Mom, get rid of her immediately." I never made a mistake like that again, and twenty years later that hard-learned lesson was still with me.

Remember: YOU are in charge. The aides work for you. They work directly with the patient, but they are not the decision makers. I consulted and asked for their advice and guidance, but the ultimate decisions were mine. Any aide who needed total control did not stay with us very long.

An Outstanding—and Previously Untrained—Aide

To my extreme good fortune, we had a wonderful housekeeper, Lizette Rodriguez, who had been with us for over a dozen years. She knew Ady's gentleness, his goodness, his thoughtfulness. She knew that he treated her with complete dignity. And she adored him. I remember one day, long before Ady's bicycle accident, when she was vacuuming in the dining room and singing. I said, "Lizette, I love to hear you sing!"

She responded, "I love my job! No one has ever treated me the way you and Mr. Berger do."

Flash forward. Ady returned from a month away after his hip surgery and came home with the aides the nursing agency sent. Lizette had no training in the care of a patient, but I knew how much she appreciated Ady. I knew how responsible, reliable, and smart she was. I took her aside and said, "Lizette, forget the house. I'd like you to follow those nurses around every minute of the day. Watch what they do and learn from them, because I'm hoping, since you care so deeply for Mr. Berger, that you will want to be doing this very soon." The aides were not too pleased. They kept asking her to leave. But, trooper that she was, Lizette hung in there, saying, "Mrs. Berger wants me to be here." After Lizette had worked for Mr. Berger all those years as her "boss," I was a little concerned that, not having been trained as a nurse, she might be uncomfortable seeing him undressed in the shower. I was stunned the first day, when it came time for the aides to get him into the shower and they again tried to dismiss Lizette, that she held her ground and stayed right in there with them.

Lizette learned from instinct, from common sense, from observation, from innate wisdom, but mostly from deep caring and love. She became Ady's chief caregiver and trained every person who came into our household. If I was away for a few hours during the day, I got a full report on my return home as to who lived up to her high standards and who did not. She was always right on target, because she wanted Ady to be surrounded by people who supported him and gave him the respect and dignity that she, too, wanted for him.

Although I had high hopes for how Lizette would work out in this new role, I could never have envisioned what a gem she would turn out to be. Today, years after Ady's passing, Lizette is still with me and, though I am blessed with health and abundant energy, she watches over me as tenderly as she did for Ady. She reminds me daily to drink more water, get out and exercise, stand up straight, and go to bed early. I never leave for a tennis game or an evening out without her telling me as I go to "have

Lizette

fun!" In recent years I receive a text each morning from Lizette, saying, "Live your life. Enjoy!"

Managing Aides and Consistency

From Ady's first day home after his hip surgery, with all his medications, complicated treatments, exercise schedule, and naps, I understood that I needed to outline a workable plan. I set out to create one. Not just for me, but for the aides who were assisting me in his care.

I began with broad rudimentary schedules but soon discovered that Ady's medications and treatments (necessitated not by Alzheimer's but by prior conditions) were so complex that no one, including me, could remember the order. Nor could we remember what time he had to finish breakfast in order to take medications, his shower, or whatever else needed to be accomplished to have him dressed and ready for his trainer. My initial attempts at a schedule were unrealistic, because I never allowed enough time for him to accomplish all that he needed to do. It was essential that he move at a leisurely pace, as the stress of being late or rushed made things worse. The simple act of putting on his support hose took ten to fifteen minutes each morning. My more realistic schedules took years to develop and refine. They were not arrived at unilaterally by me sitting in front of a computer. Mostly I developed them with Lizette, who always had the most practical solutions. But we encouraged each of the aides to express what he or she thought would work best, and their suggestions were often excellent.

Consistency was important for Ady—not just after his diagnosis, but all his life. He would become easily rattled by new surroundings or schedules. It was important that, no matter who was on duty, Ady could expect the same routine with the chart that we fondly called "the Bible." This consistency was a source of great comfort for him and for me as well. It meant that while his aides might change, his routine did not. I depended on the various schedules for my own use as well. If these schedules appear rigid and inflexible, they were; they had to be. But within the confines of the printed schedule, we all had to be open, creative, and flexible.

Scheduling the Aides

In order to keep track of which aide was on duty and when, I worked out the schedules with their availability in mind. Other than Lizette, each aide had her own family commitments, responsibilities, children's activities, and family vacations.

The only way we could keep it straight was for me to make elaborate charts at least a month in advance. Conflicts that arose as I was creating the monthly chart required many phone calls back and forth. The charts were posted at home, and each aide took a copy home as it was revised. Each aide had the others' phone numbers, so they could communicate and replace themselves with another trained aide if they had an unexpected conflict. To further make certain that there was no miscommunication or confusion, I color-coded the charts, giving each aide her own color so she could tell at a glance when she was on duty. The following page shows a sample of the chart I developed in coordination with each, showing the date, different shifts, and comments.

Heading the charts were each aide's name, email, and phone number. Each column in the chart showed the date, times, and names of the aides on early and late shift, and any special events or appointments that were expected that day. Each aide was highlighted in her own color, so she could see immediately when she was working, and I always included each aide's specific times, because their times would often vary depending on their schedule. The standard shifts were approximately 7 hours: from 8:00 A.M.

AIDE CHART FALL 2010

Name	Email	Phone
Lizette	###	###
Mershelle	###	###
Marilyn	###	###

Date	Name	Early Time	Name	Later Time	Event with Ady
Sat Aug 28	Lizette	8 am–3 pm	Mershelle	3 pm–10 pm	
Sun Aug 28	Lizette	8 am–3 pm	Mershelle	3 pm–10 pm	
Mon Aug 30	Mershelle	8 am–10 pm			
Tues Aug 31	Lizette	8–1, 7–10	Marilyn	1 pm–7 pm	
Wed Sept 1	Lizette	8 am–3 pm	Mershelle	3 pm–10 pm	
Thurs Sept 2	Lizette	8 am–3 pm	Mershelle	3 pm–10 pm	
Fri Sept 3	Lizette	8 am–3 pm	Mershelle	3 pm–10 pm	
Sat Sept 4	Lizette	8 am–3 pm	Mershelle	3 pm–10 pm	
Sun Sept 5	Lizette	all day			concert @ 3 pm Lizette
Mon Sept 6	Lizette	8 am–3 pm	Mershelle	3 pm–10 pm	
Tues Sept 7	Lizette	8 am–4pm	Mershelle	4 pm–10pm	
Wed Sept 8	Lizette	all day			H to Bos Rosh Hashana
Thurs Sept 9	Lizette	8 am–4pm	Mershelle	4 pm–10pm	H ret from Boston
Fri Sept 10	Lizette	all day			temple with Ady
Sat Sept 11	Mershelle	8 am–3 pm	Lizette	3 pm–10 pm	
Sun Sept 12	Lizette	all day			concert @ 3 pm Lizette
Mon Sept 13	Mershelle	8 am–3 pm	Marilyn	3 pm–10 pm	
Tues Sept 14	Lizette	8 am–3 pm	Marilyn	3 pm–10 pm	
Wed Sept 15	Lizette	8 am–3 pm	Marilyn	3 pm–10 pm	3 pm–10 pm
Thu Sept 16	Lizette	8 am–4pm	Mershelle	4 pm–10pm	
Fri Sept 17	Lizette	all day			Kol Nidre dinner home
Sat Sept 18	Lizette	8 am–4pm	Mershelle	4 pm–10pm	Yom Kippur
Sun Sept 19	Lizette	all day			concert @ 3 pm Lizette
Mon Sept 20	Mershelle	8 am–3 pm	Marilyn	3 pm–10 pm	
Tues Sept 21	Mershelle	8 am–3 pm	Marilyn	3 pm–10 pm	
Wed Sept 22	Mershelle	8 am–3 pm	Marilyn	3 pm–10 pm	
Thu Sept 23	Mershelle	all day			
Fri Sept 24	Lizette	all day			
Sat Sept 25	Mershelle	8 am–2 pm	Lizette	2 pm–10 pm	
Sun Sept 26	Lizette	all day			concert @ 3 pm Lizette
Mon Sept 27	Lizette	8: am–1 pm	Marilyn	1 pm–10 pm	
Tues Sept 28	Lizette	8 am–3 pm	Mershelle	3 pm–10 pm	
Wed Sept 29	Lizette	8 am–3 pm	Mershelle	3 pm–10 pm	
Thu Sept 30	Lizette	8 am–3 pm	Marilyn	3 pm–10 pm	
Fri Oct 1	Lizette	8 am–3 pm	Marilyn	3 pm–10 pm	
Sat Oct 2	Lizette	8 am–3 pm	Marilyn	3 pm–10 pm	
Sun Oct 3	Lizette	all day			concert @ 3 pm Lizette

to 3:00 P.M. and from 3:00 P.M. until approximately 10:00 P.M. (unless Ady was ready for bed earlier).

With this chart, no one ever said to me, "I'm sorry, I thought I was on from four o'clock today!" My theory, as in all things in life, was to put in the time and energy in advance rather than panic in the present by being unprepared.

Dismissing Unsatisfactory Aides

At first it was very difficult for me to let someone go. I agonized over what to say in an effort to be polite and kind. Over the years I had to do it so many times that it became easier. My priorities were clear: the few uncomfortable minutes to dismiss someone who was clearly not working out were insignificant compared to what was best for my husband. Sometimes the person I was letting go reacted with a stream of ugly anger; that only reinforced my decision. Earlier in the process I would try to hang on, hoping that the person would change after I had a talk with her. With time, I learned that such changes never happened. Living so closely with the wrong person, one who did not have Ady's best interests at heart, increased my stress level. I finally understood not to prolong what would never be right.

Every experience is different, and every reason for letting someone go is different. Here is one example of a seemingly responsible woman who came to us well recommended. At first, I thought she was a positive addition to the team. After about two weeks of her working with us, Lizette, whose judgment I always trusted, came to me and told me that Nancy (not her real name) was not the right person for Mr. Berger. I was surprised and asked why. She is two-faced, Lizette said. "She's very nice to Mr. Berger when you're around, but she pays no attention to him and does not speak to him or encourage him when you're not." Since my own observations were different, I told Lizette that I'd like to observe her for at least another week.

The opportunity to see the reality in action occurred the next day. I came up to the apartment after a tennis game and called, "Hello!" No one answered. Ady was asleep; the aide, apparently, had not heard me. I went into my closet to change and get ready for a shower. While I was in the closet, Ady awakened and called to the kitchen for assistance. Instead of revealing my presence, I turned off the closet light and kept the door open about half an inch, which afforded me a clear view of Ady's bed. What I saw was a revelation. Nancy walked in without a word. No greeting. No simple question like, "Did you have a nice nap?" In silence she rather roughly changed the diaper and got him out of bed. Not one word was spoken in the ten or fifteen minutes it took to get him out of bed.

I was appalled. I chose not to reveal myself and confront her then, as I did not trust her there for the rest of the day around Ady if she knew that she was to be let go. But my decision was clear. My own observation, coupled with Lizette's report, told me everything I needed to know. That night when I told Ady that she would not be coming back, he looked at me with a smile and said, "Good!" I tried to encourage him to speak up in the future if something was not right, but the chances of him doing so were remote.

Nancy was off the following day, with another aide covering. The next morning, I called and asked her to come in so I could talk to her. "Why?" she asked.

"I'd rather speak to you in person." When I took her privately into a room and sat her down, all I said was, "Nancy, I'm sorry, but this is not working out for me."

This is an important point. What I learned in the course of dismissing others is that *simple is best.* I had plenty of long talks with others who I thought had potential, telling them what I'd like to see changed. Some were appreciative and made an effort to change, but most did not. With Nancy, especially, I did not feel obligated to give any reason. She would have vociferously rejected any words that I might have said and left even angrier. She kept asking me, "Why?" and like a broken record I just kept repeating, "It's just not working for me." I presented her with a check for that week and the following week's salary. She took it and left in anger. The fact that it was not good for me or for Ady was all that mattered.

Empowering Your Aide

The example of how to treat those who work to help you was set for me as a young child. Since both my parents worked when I was young, we had housekeepers. My parents always treated the housekeepers with the greatest respect and appreciation. Later in life, when I had occasion to see how some people treated their "maids," I was shocked and lost respect for them, no matter how many good deeds they did in the public eye.

I depended greatly on the aides, and I valued the people who helped me with Ady, often in the most intimate ways. I believe they all knew my affection for them and certainly my appreciation. I bent over backwards to consult with them and listen to their suggestions. I made sure they saw those daily charts not as a rule book but rather as a help, like a friend standing by to give support and guidance. No one began work for us without Lizette standing by for at least their first two days on the job, explaining in detail our many systems and procedures. Mastering Ady's care would have been overwhelming without learning from a caring colleague.

I always spent time talking with the people helping us, about their lives, their families, and their troubles. I tried to achieve the difficult and delicate balance between being "the boss" imposing her will and being open to listening and to learning—while at the same time expressing my authority to ensure quality and consistency of care. Most of the aides who were with us for a long time recognized that while my top priority was making Ady's life as good as it could be, I genuinely cared about them as well.

Just as I learned the magic of praise with Ady, when an aide came up with an innovative suggestion, as they did so often, I acknowledged the contribution and expressed how pleased I was. I recognized talent and learned from those who had something positive to impart. Her idea would be immediately incorporated into our routine. We made constant adjustments as different situations evolved on a daily basis. Even for those who are trained as aides, every case is different. It takes creative solutions and ingenuity to determine what is best for each patient. We were constantly learning how to manage situations we had never before envisioned.

CHAPTER TEN

The Doctor-Patient-Caregiver Partnership

THE PARTNERSHIP THAT WE ESTABLISHED WITH ADY'S many doctors was vitally important for his progress, his hope, and his self-esteem. The essence of this chapter is how to develop and encourage the doctor-patient-caregiver partnership. The two sides of the coin were my role as advocate for the patient and the doctor's important role in response.

First, the patient / advocate's role in the partnership. In our earlier years as a couple, when we had more than our share of Ady's surgeries and medical conditions, I developed systems that worked for us at home and made his doctor's role easier and more satisfying. Below is a summary of these procedures.

What to Bring to Every Appointment

1. List of patient's current medications, including:

Name of medication
Doses
Times per day

- Color-coding to indicate which were pills and which were treatments (in our case, nebulizers, vibrating vest, and various sprays)

I know how helpful doctors found this because of how often they would ask me if they could remove Ady's name and specific medications and give their patients a copy of my chart, to encourage them to keep similar charts.

2. List of all past surgeries and conditions

These were already on Ady's medical chart, but bringing it saved the doctors time and refreshed their memories. A copy of Ady's surgery and condition list for the doctors follows.

LIST OF SURGERIES & CONDITIONS

ADOLPH J. BERGER

January 28, 2010

PRIOR SURGERIES

1966	Lobectomy RLL (Bronchiectasis)
1974	Sinus surgery (Caldwell-Luc)
1988	Hip fracture (Sub capita fracture left femur)
	TURP (BPH)
	Phlebitis (left leg)
1991	Herniated disc—L2, L3 (no surgery)
1994	Radical retropubic prostatectomy
9/29/99	Angioplasty with stent (Circumflex artery)
5/19/00	Prepatellar bursitis right knee (removed)
10/30/00	Hernioplasty (left inguinal hernia repair)
3/11/05	Pneumonia / Pulmonary embolism
3/12/05	Greenfield filter inferior vena cava (followed by six months of Coumadin; now on 5 mg daily Coumadin)
5/8/05	Angioplasty (negative result)

11/2008	Cellulitis—right leg
1/27/09	Partial hip replacement (fell 1/25/09—fractured hip)
12/3/09	Benign scalp verrucous acanthoma removed via Mohs surgery Squamous cell carcinoma

CONDITIONS

Bronchiectasis

As of Dec, 2010, lungs in good shape with daily treatments on Medication chart

(Numerous pneumonias. On 3/11/05 as noted above **Pulmonary Embolism** and another Pneumonia on Oct 20, 2005. Hospitalized 4 days followed by PICC line with Zosyn 13.5 mg four times per day for 3 weeks.)

Possible Pneumonia 6/7/06 treated with Ceftriaxone IV (heparin lock 7 days)

Pneumonia BMC Hospital Oct 2, 2007, five days (culture Pseudomonas, Pneumococci) Ceftazidime 2 gm / 20 ml 2 wks after discharge + Azithromycin 500 2 wks

Asthma

Hiatal Hernia

Reflux Esophagitis

Reactive Hypoglycemia

Alzheimer's

Walks with walker—Wheel chair for any distance

Incontinence (bowel & urinary)

Constant fatigue (improved greatly with Provigil)

Tremor in hands (better on current medication)

50% Tear in right Achilles tendon (probable cause: large doses Cipro)

Feb 2007 after **FALL,** hand fracture (small [fifth] metacarpal fracture)

See MEDICATION LIST (Nebulizer treatments 3x daily, Vibrating Vest 2x daily

Active exercise program

Ady is <u>NOT</u> to take: Cipro, Levaquin, or Avalox due to the effect on his Achilles tendon as of May 2006

---

3. Current spreadsheet list of all doctors

I always gave the doctors a copy of this list. At the top of the list was Ady's name, address, date of birth, and other pertinent information. The list itself was a simple one-page spreadsheet as shown below. The last two columns (when was our last appointment and when Ady was due for his next one) were a crucial tool for me that I still keep for myself. Don't we all feel that we had our last colonoscopy two years ago, when it's really been five and we're due for the next one? Or that we were just at the periodontist last month, when it's actually been four? The key is to look at the list periodically to make sure we're on track. (Today I would probably use digital reminders as well.)

At the end of the doctor's list was the phone number of the pharmacy, along with a list and date of various shots like flu, pneumonia, tetanus, etc.

When formatted like this, one page carries a wealth of pertinent information.

DOCTORS FOR ADY						
NAME: last first, alphabetical order	Specialty	Address	Phone/ Fax	Sec/ Nurse	Last Appt	Due Next

4. One-page copy of all patient's pertinent cards

Driver's license
Medicare info
Social Security number. (If you choose not to include your patient's social security number for fear of identity theft,

it's a good idea to have it in your wallet, as most hospitals require it.)

Insurance info

AARP (or secondary insurance)

5. Written list of any issues for discussion

The list should include the date the problem began, along with concerns and questions. I always brought a copy for both the doctor and me, so we could review the list together. This was a great time-saver for the doctor, making sure we spent every minute of our appointment on essentials, rather than wasting time groping through charts and our memories to ascertain the sequence of events.

Four of those lists—Medications, Doctors, Surgeries and Conditions, and Vital Information Cards—were always in an envelope taped to the refrigerator and in the glove compartment of our car so we always had them with us. When Ady did fall and fracture his hip, that envelope on the refrigerator was a godsend. There was no way I could have begun, in the midst of the stress in the immediate aftermath of his fall, to round up all the essential information. Because Ady was a very complicated case, in addition to the above envelope, there was a large sign posted on the refrigerator door that read:

> IF AMBULANCE NEEDED: Unless it is a life or death situation, PLEASE TAKE MR. BERGER ONLY TO MT. SINAI HOSPITAL IN MIAMI BEACH. ALL OF MR. BERGER'S DOCTORS AND MEDICAL RECORDS ARE AT MT. SINAI. Especially if I am not home, he must go there, because no aide is equipped to answer all questions at another hospital.
>
> THANK YOU

The Patient-Doctor Partnership in Action

The doctors had a great fondness for Ady's gentle way, his sweet smile, and his verbal expression of appreciation. In the early days they appreciated his keen grasp of medical issues and options, as well as his strict adherence to the regime they prescribed—no matter how complicated. They also knew that I had my finger on the pulse of Ady's case.

For example, Ady's lungs were always his weak spot, with numerous pneumonias requiring IV with a PICC line. I remember a phone call on a late Friday afternoon to his pulmonologist. I said, "I don't like the way Ady sounds, even though he's not bringing up anything messy." The doctor knew that I never called with a trivial concern, and that I understood Ady's symptoms. His immediate response was, "If you're detecting something, I'll prescribe the antibiotic that has been successful in the past." Two days later, the green gunk and labored breathing started. Though the doctor had to add an additional antibiotic, it was the first time Ady had dodged the bullet and avoided pneumonia because the course of action had begun so early. This was a doctor-patient partnership at its best!

The physicians showed their respect and caring in many ways. For example, at appointments during the later years, when Ady was less engaged, each of his doctors showed respect for Ady in a subtle but important way—by always addressing him first, asking for his assessment of his condition. They would wait until Ady was completely finished with his report before turning to me for my additional comments. And I learned not to interrupt his remarks, keeping silent until he completed what he wanted to say.

That simple courtesy (so often skipped—especially with Alzheimer's patients) was deeply important in helping Ady maintain his dignity. He did not sit back like an outside bystander as we discussed his condition. If your doctors address their questions to you first, you might want to consider a nod towards your patient, suggesting that they begin with him.

Another conversation that is branded indelibly in my memory took place in the hospital the night before Ady's emergency hip fracture surgery. His surgeon, Dr. Marc Umlas (whom I had just met the night before), said, "When Ady returns to his room after surgery tomorrow, he'll be very groggy. I want you to come in the morning with enlarged photos of Ady and his family and hang them on the wall."

I responded, "What a lovely idea—so he begins to focus and remember!"

"*No*," he said. "It's not for Ady. I want every doctor, nurse, aide, or the person who delivers his meals to see those photos and know that this is not an 'out of it' old man. I want them to know who he is and see a vibrant, active man with a loving family."

I stayed up late that night to select the photos from my computer and print them out on 8" by 10" sheets so they could be viewed across the room. They worked like magic. Every hospital person entering the room stopped to view them and looked at Ady with vastly more compassion than they might have.

That is only one example of the deep kindness and devoted interest that Ady experienced from each of our doctors. They praised him at each office visit for how beautifully he was doing, and he lit up with their compliments. When there were worrisome medical issues, we got phone calls from his doctors at home inquiring how he was doing.

The doctors were equally supportive of me, letting me know in a multitude of ways what a great job they felt I was doing. Witnessing Ady's stunning progress, they were actually the ones early on who encouraged me to write about what I had learned, expressing how helpful they felt it would be for others. Though I had been taking notes for myself throughout the experience, I never dreamed about shaping my notes into a book. It was the doctors' early encouragement, coupled with those of friends who made similar requests, that planted the seed and motivated me to proceed.

I believe that a large part of Ady's success was due to the cooperation between us and his doctors. When doctors see caring and actively involved spouses and family members who are acting responsibly, their natural response is to become more engaged, more giving of themselves and their time, and more willing to work with you closely as part of your team. Each of Ady's doctors expressed support and encouragement to me as well, giving me the confidence that my judgement was sound and that Ady was responding beautifully to the care he was receiving.

CHAPTER ELEVEN

Coping with Setbacks and Emergencies

I'VE BEEN DESCRIBING THE POSSIBILITIES FOR JOY AND beauty in our lives despite the bleak circumstances. Perhaps a reality check is due here. It's crucial to understand that this experience, no matter how many positive strides you are making, will have periods of frustration, sadness, anxiety, and emotional stress. There will surely be setbacks along the way—setbacks that make you want to crawl into a corner and cry. Some setbacks are quietly harrowing; others are genuine emergencies demanding immediate action. Both bring times of great stress and pressure.

Every story of Alzheimer's, no matter how hopeful, is a story of decline. That decline is often not linear but in steps; some event precipitates a noticeable decline, large or small, in abilities and in options. Both patient and caregiver are thrown. How does the caregiver cope—externally and internally? How does she keep from falling into despair? How does she go back to square one and learn acceptance once again?

Expect Setbacks

I will share one example of a deeply distressing setback that took us all by surprise.

With Ady's background as one who swam on the Dartmouth swim team and who took pride in his ability in the water even many years into Alzheimer's, I was stunned and saddened during the last several years to witness a mental block that arose each time he asked to go for a swim. This occurred during the period when he was doing remarkably well in all other areas—when his cognition was beyond all expectations. Swimming had been Ady's lifelong choice of exercise. He *wanted* to swim. He insisted on getting into his bathing suit and being taken down to the pool. Then, one day, he stood on the first few steps of the pool—and then froze. He literally could not get in. He was terrified of getting into the water. He began to shiver, and when we urged him to try it on another day, he refused to come back out.

One weekend when our daughter visited, he asked her to come down to the pool with him. Knowing how he adored her and would do virtually anything to make her happy, I was certain that he would plunge right in. It was harrowing for her to plead with him and watch him stand there for over two hours, unwilling to go in and unwilling to leave the water. A few weeks later, with his repeated insistence that he go down to the pool for a swim, he got so chilled standing up to his knees in the water that he came down with a severe pneumonia.

I don't think that I ever was able to accept this behavior. Each time we tried to dissuade him from going to the pool, knowing the hours that were in store for us, he absolutely insisted. He promised that this time he would go in, but he simply could not. Watching him in this unending struggle was difficult. We were all exhausted by what became an almost daily heartbreaking ritual. We pleaded with him not to go down to the pool as he begged us to take him, promising that this time he'd get right in. We even offered him a life vest—all to no avail.

I describe this emotionally draining experience to say that no matter how much effort we caregivers put in, no matter how positive the successes are, there will surely be failures along the way. Had this behavior occurred during the early years, it would have been an understandable part of what comes with Alzheimer's. Occurring as it did, when he had made such inexplicably positive strides, it was devastating. Ady was still so rational about most things that this felt like a significant setback for all of us. I describe it here to reinforce that no matter how much progress seems to take place, there will be setbacks. Hopefully, the more armed you are with the expectation that they will occur, the less shocking they will be, and the more emotionally prepared you will be to handle them.

Facing Emergencies

The following description probably represents our lowest ebb, but I tell it because I think there were many important lessons along the way. The emergency took place three and a half years after the official diagnosis, before we had the need for aides at home, as Ady and I were still comfortable with him being alone for short periods. I came up from my daily walk, stopped by the kitchen on my way to the bedroom, and turned on the water to soak my socks. I had plugged up the sink and began to fill it with water when I thought I heard a cry for help from the bathroom. I raced out of the kitchen and found Ady lying on the floor, unable to get up. He had fallen on the hard-tiled bathroom floor. There was no possibility of my lifting him alone.

Fortunately, we lived in an apartment that had valets, as is common in Florida condominiums. I called for help. The valet arrived quickly and with great difficulty lifted Ady into the chair in his bathroom. It was clear that this was serious. Ady was barely moving, and his head was bleeding from the fall. The valet stayed for about ten minutes until Ady seemed to be okay. As he was preparing to leave, I left Ady in the chair as I went to call for an ambulance. As I did, I passed by the kitchen—which was now flooded with more than an inch of water. We are all familiar with the idiom "it never rains but it pours!" I do believe that when misfortune or difficult situations happen, they tend to follow each other in rapid succession.

I called for the ambulance, and the valet helped me mop up the water, using most of the towels in the house. I kept running in to check on Ady and urging myself to stay calm. Over and over I admonished myself: *this is* not *the time to panic.*

The second call I made was to alert the emergency room at Mount Sinai that we were on our way. All of Ady's doctors were affiliated there, and Mount Sinai had all of his voluminous records. But convincing the ambulance paramedic to take Ady to Mount Sinai was a challenge: the hospital was at least twenty minutes away, whereas there was a local hospital about three blocks away. I understood that ambulances were instructed to take every patient to the nearest hospital, but I explained to the attendant that Ady's medical records were very complicated and asked if he could please take him to Mount Sinai. The paramedic looked at me, trying to size up the situation, and then asked to see Ady and assess his condition. If Ady had been unconscious, he would have had no choice but to take him to the closest hospital. Fortunately, Ady was alert and calm. After checking his vital signs, the paramedic agreed to take Ady to Mount Sinai. They took him down on a stretcher.

Being Prepared in Advance

Still in my jogging clothes, I grabbed both my purse and the emergency envelope that I kept taped to the refrigerator in readiness for a time like this, which contained the four documents I described in Chapter 10:

- Copies of all Ady's identification records: Medicare plan, driver's license, Social Security number
- A list of Ady's surgeries and conditions
- A list of all his medications
- A list of all his doctors (with specialty, address, and phone number)

As I expressed earlier, under this kind of pressure and stress I could never have begun to round up these essential documents. All were critically needed if Ady was to be dealt with efficiently and effectively. Having those emergency documents ready without a frantic search helped a great deal to keep things under control. Just as in preparing for a hurricane, the more we can prepare in advance for any eventuality, the easier problems will be to deal with when they occur.

Managing Your Fears to Maintain External Calm

Then came the next hurdle. As they were getting Ady into the ambulance, the paramedic, who was extremely polite and sympathetic, said, "Mrs. Berger, I'm sorry, but you'll have to ride up front with the driver. You are not allowed to ride with him in the ambulance. I'll be with him."

Although my own blood pressure must have been soaring at that point, I mustered up a totally calm exterior and quietly said, "Sir, we have been married for fifty-two years. You'll have a much calmer patient if I can be near him."

He looked at me for what seemed an eternity as my eyes never left his. Then he said, "I'm not supposed to do this, but okay. Climb in." I knew instinctively that if he thought he had a hysterical, emotional woman on his hands whom he would have to attend to in addition to his patient, he never would have broken the rules.

During the ride, I did, in fact, hold Ady's hand and talk to him quietly to keep him calm. When I sensed that this kind paramedic, who was sitting in back with us, understood that he had made the decision that was most beneficial to his patient, I pulled out the charts in my envelope and showed them to him.

He said, "I've never seen anything like this before!"

I cannot begin to describe the emotional distress that I was experiencing during this episode. When I later asked the nurse in the hospital to take my blood pressure, it was dangerously high. I felt like Anna in *The King and I,* who whistled a happy tune in an attempt to fool others—and herself—into believing she is not afraid. My determination to maintain outward calm enabled me to ride with Ady in the ambulance and to have him taken to the hospital of my choice.

Knowing Whom to Call

I made two calls in the ambulance. The first was to our son in Philadelphia, letting him know that I was in the ambulance on the way to the hospital, anticipating that Dad probably had a hip fracture. The second call was to my lifelong friend, Elaine Bloom, who lived on Miami Beach not far from the hospital. She arrived shortly after we did and stayed by my side for nine hours—comforting me, getting me food, calling doctors, getting nurses to respond, and letting me know that I was not alone. When we left at 3:20 A.M. Elaine insisted on driving me back to Miami.

I knew that our lives, once again, were forever changed. But I understood something else as well: We all know how nice it is to have friends. We have fun with our friends. We go out to dinner or a movie, we play games, we watch sports, we laugh with them and learn from them. Especially when you live in a city away from family, your friends become your extended family and are an important part of your life. But at times like the emergency I just described, I understood the crucial value of real friendships built over a lifetime. I understood what it means to have friends who are there for you when you are not able to function. I held myself together until I got to the hospital and then, knowing that I was in such capable hands, let Elaine take over for me in arranging for the surgery the next day and every other detail. I sat numbly watching her find food for me in the middle of the night and follow through on everything that needed to be accomplished.

It's important that we have those people in our lives—either family or friends, people you can depend on, whom you trust to take over when you're not functioning at an optimal level. Our son, Mark (a cardiologist) flew in from Philadelphia, arriving early the next morning and heading directly to the hospital. He got there in time to discuss the options with the surgeon in advance of the surgery. I would not have understood nor been in a position to make those crucial decisions about which of the options would have been best. Our daughter, Bonnie, was on the phone constantly with her concern, support, and love.

Combating Loneliness

Again, I realize how fortunate I am. Years after Ady's passing, I read an article in the *Washington Post* that corroborated what I've just described. It quoted the former U.S. Surgeon General, Dr. Vivek H. Murthy, who spoke of a "loneliness epidemic." The Surgeon General went on: "We live in the most technologically connected age in the history of civilization, yet rates of loneliness have doubled since the 1980s." In addition to the typical physical concerns, he describes emotional well-being and loneliness as big public-health worries. According to Dr. Murthy, data shows that even compared to tobacco use and obesity, "you'll find loneliness is associated with a greater risk of heart disease, depression, anxiety, and dementia."*

Without realizing it, throughout my experience with Ady during the Alzheimer's years, I had built a support system of people I could count on: the doctors, my family (even though they did not live near me), friends, and Lizette. At the time of the harrowing emergency described above, even the valet at the building we live in, Mirko, knew us and was more than willing to help. Our son, Mark, our daughter, Bonnie, Elaine and our other friends all boosted me every day. I did not feel alone. I felt connected to a caring family.

I encourage you to build the relationships and think in advance of the people you might call upon in moments of stress or when you need a shoulder to cry on. Who is physically closest? Who is the most knowledgeable and empowered to share in the family decisions? Who is the friend you can rely on when your own resources are exhausted?

. . .

Though your emergencies will surely be different than mine, know that they will happen. Decline in a person suffering with Alzheimer's, either physical, mental, or emotional, will occur. Looking back, you will be able to pinpoint the events where significant additional decline took place. When we can anticipate these changes, we will be less likely to be thrown by them, and better prepared to handle the most difficult times.

* Jena McGregor, "This former surgeon general says there's a 'loneliness epidemic' and work is partly to blame." *Washington Post,* October 4, 2017.

CHAPTER TWELVE

Giving Yourself What You Need

Seeking Balance

THE CONTENT OF THIS BOOK SO FAR HAS FOCUSED ON what we can do to improve the quality of our loved one's life. It is equally important to understand what *we* need, to act on those needs, and to seek balance in our own lives. Even if you've chosen to give your all to your loved one, that doesn't mean you have to stop living. If you do, you will both be the losers. Finding that balance is not easy and will be different for every person and each couple.

Continuing to Live Your Life

The decision to live one's own life, given the circumstances of a declining mate, is not easy. It is, however, a decision, or rather multiple decisions, that must be made with conscious choice.

I doubt I would have come to this crucial understanding without the excellent professional guidance that I was blessed to have.

The message was clear: "DO NOT STOP LIVING YOUR LIFE. It will not be good for you, and it will certainly not be good for Ady. The moment you feel trapped, a host of other negative qualities and unhealthy emotions—resentment, anger, impatience, irritability—will begin to creep in."

I know that I was blessed. Ady was genuinely happy for me to continue to experience all that I could in life. From what I've observed in other couples, when one is declining (even in couples who lived full and independent lives in the past), there is a tendency for the declining mate to become demanding of the caregiving mate's full-time presence and attention. Both patient and caregiver need to truly understand that caregivers cannot give that kind of support and encouragement if they're on duty twenty-four seven. Caregivers need to find a way to create some precious time alone each day.

DISCUSSING YOUR COLLECTIVE WELL-BEING

When making a choice, be sure to clarify, well in advance, that both you and your loved one are on the same page. Consistency is important for the patient as well as for you. I wouldn't have wanted to renegotiate each time I wanted to play tennis whether it was okay for both Ady and for me. It may have seemed like a luxury, but I determined it was important for my well-being (and therefore for both of us), and I gave myself permission to enjoy it. (The apartment building we lived in had tennis courts, so I was always on the premises if needed. I was usually back with Ady within a little over an hour.)

The ground rules for "permission" to continue to live must be set early on, before demands become entrenched. It is very difficult to break habitual behavior. What worked for me early on was an honest, open expression of why taking time for a walk, or to be with friends, enabled me to be there for Ady more fully. I explained that I wanted to be there for him in every possible way, but I did not want to feel cut off from life.

Your past outside interests, activities, and involvement will be your guide. One must, of course, consider your financial ability to get the essential help you need for you to remain whole. If there are financial constraints to arranging the alone or apart time, try to find family or friends who can help to give you a respite. Be creative in carving out the hours you need to stay sane. In the early stages, before symptoms are more pronounced or worrisome, it might even work to have a responsible teenager come in after school for an hour to play checkers, chess, cards, or whatever they both might enjoy so you can get out for a walk. The moment the balance scale tips too heavily to one side, it should be a bright yellow caution light for you to seek a correction. Only you can determine what that balance is for you. No one else can define it.

Another variable in the equation when caring for a spouse is the nature of your past relationship. What are his or her needs and expectations? If those needs are demanding, especially of your constant presence, I would urge you to put on your own oxygen mask first. The kind of conversation I described, about why your continuing to be part of the world is important to both of you, may have to take place many times. The more it is expressed with gentleness and kindness and a sense of working together, rather than as a demand on your part, the more likely it is to be understood and accepted.

Exercise

I spoke earlier of the need for your patient to exercise. Exercise is equally essential for the caregiver—even if you've never exercised before. I'm not talking about anything strenuous: you do not need to endure a challenging workout unless you wish to do so. Just a simple daily (or at least three times a week) walk will go a very long way to improving your physical health and emotional well-being. Every article on the subject emphasizes the positive impact of exercise on health and state of mind. Many of these articles claim that exercise is more effective than the most powerful anti-anxiety drugs. When Ady was in the hospital and rehab for a month after surgery for his hip fracture, our son, a cardiologist, told me, "Mom, I don't want you going to the hospital without first playing tennis or exercising. This is not a suggestion but a prescription." He was absolutely right. With his blessing, I played tennis without guilt and arrived eagerly at the hospital ready to tackle whatever was in store for me.

I believe I was receptive to the advice of my son, my therapist, and others not to shut down my life because of an important example that was set for me—an example both positive and negative.

A little over a year after I lost my mother, my father, who was still practicing dentistry in Brooklyn, married another extraordinary woman. I was delighted with his choice and thrilled to see my dad come to life again after my mother's long illness. He and his second wife had seventeen years of a good marriage, full of travel and music and theater. Then my father had a stroke, which left his body half paralyzed but his mind intact.

My stepmother devoted herself totally to my dad after his stroke. For ten years she *never* missed a day of visiting him in the nursing home for at least six hours a day, bringing him gourmet dinners and creating a world of beauty in that dismal place. In the early years, friends would call and beg her to join them for dinner. The answer was always the same: "I couldn't possibly. I have to come home and cook Sid's dinner, and I'll be much too tired." They would call again and again, until eventually they gave up. In my many trips to the city, I was the only one with whom she ever went out to dinner.

This was great for my father, who received the benefits of her devoted care, but my stepmother, who was a beautiful, vital, well-read, worldly, knowledgeable woman, became dried up and bitter. After my dad passed away, other than my daily calls to her from Miami, my frequent visits, and the round-the-clock nurses that she soon needed, she cut herself off totally from the world. She spent her days sitting in her special reclining chair (after trying four others first) and ordering "stuff" from catalogues—90 percent of which she returned. She eventually had a stroke and we moved her to Miami, where I could be closer to her.

I watched a vibrant woman make a choice to stop living her own life—and I determined never to make that same mistake. In retrospect, it was an important example for me of what *not* to become.

What I gradually learned was to try to give Ady everything he needed to keep him happy, healthy, cared for, and feeling loved and appreciated—without totally sacrificing my own life. I knew how blessed I was with the gift of health and life, and though I accepted that my life was vastly changed, I chose not to devote 100 percent of my time to caring for Ady, as was my instinct. I continuously sought healthy, wholesome, enriching joy and laughter wherever I could find it. For me, that was often on the tennis court, where I could laugh with friends and focus my full attention and energy on hitting that ball. For you it might be something else, but the importance of living your own life remains.

It is easy to shut down along with the person you love. One problem is that the habits of living are difficult to reengage: when one shuts down on life, it is not easy to restart later. Of more immediate relevance, however, is that I'm convinced that I would not have been capable of giving Ady the loving care that I did if I felt cheated out of life. When I felt fulfilled by a workout or an event I attended, I would come home eager to spend meaningful time with him and looking forward to our evening activity together—encouraging him to draw, sitting together to do a

Sudoku puzzle, or playing chess together. Those were happy times for both of us—and I didn't feel resentment, because I had spent a small portion of my day away from the enervating responsibility of caretaking.

The situation I witnessed with my stepmother was reinforced by a *New York Times* article that I recently encountered entitled, "Caregiving Is Hard Enough. Isolation Can Make It Unbearable."* The woman profiled in the article speaks about how "hurtful" it was to deal with the social isolation brought on by caring for her husband, who had Alzheimer's. "We hardly go anywhere, and nobody comes here," her daughter is quoted as saying. However inadvertently, Ady and I seemed to have hit on the right solution. Brief encounters, like the ones I described when we went to concerts, seemed to give him important social contact without taxing him. They turned out to be best for our friends, as well, who had a genuine love for him and were happy to have those brief exchanges of smiles and hugs.

Ten Pathways to Caregiver Self-Fulfillment

Here are ten pathways that enabled me to live as fully as possible within the confines of my new role, despite the constant inner sadness—to remain at least partially connected to my world of community involvement, friends, culture, and beauty. I didn't want this earthshaking change to make me lose my joyful reaction to the little things that made me happy in life: a rainbow, a flower, a sunset, a full moon, or the sounds of music or water running in a brook. I think of the lines from the brief poem by William Wordsworth:

---

* Paula Span, *New York Times,* August 4, 2017. https://www.nytimes.com/2017/08/04/health/caregiving-alzheimers-isolation.html

My heart leaps up when I behold
 A rainbow in the sky:
So was it when my life began;
So is it now I am a man;
So be it when I shall grow old,
 Or let me die! *

1. Finding Capable Help

I have already stated that I had no additional help for the first three and a half years. Your own story will vary, but sooner or later all of us need backup—and find it amazingly liberating when we do manage to get it. What would happen if you had a fall or an injury or illness that put you in the hospital? In our last two and a half years together, after Ady's hip surgery, finding caring, capable, supportive staff enabled me to continue to live as fully as possible under the circumstances—and to deliver better care to Ady.

2. Taking Care of Your Mental Health

By far the most significant help for me was having an excellent psychiatrist, Dr. Rees, who guided me through coping with the changes in my life in a realistic and constructive way. She encouraged me to be in touch with my emotions. It was Dr. Rees who got me to think in terms of keeping not just Ady whole, but myself as well. It was exhilaratingly liberating to give myself permission to live as fully as possible. Ady, too, was thriving, and I was better able to feel proud of my role in encouraging his progress.

3. Finding Time Alone

At one session, Dr. Rees asked, "How much alone time do you give yourself each day?"

---

* William Wordsworth, "My Heart Leaps Up."

I had not really thought about it. My answer was, "Very little." I was caring for Ady from morning to night. When I went for a walk, it was almost never alone. When I drove or was on the elliptical machine, I was usually listening to a book on tape.

The psychiatrist suggested that I give myself time to grieve for the loss I was living through. She encouraged me not to shut out the reality I was facing: to walk alone sometimes, or to be on the exercise machines *without* the book on tape.

While I always tried to follow her sound advice, I was not very successful here. I think I did not want, or was not ready, to face what lay ahead. I was so focused on Ady's progress that my inner thoughts were still almost exclusively occupied with questions like: How can I keep him on this excellent path? How can I make it better for him and for us?

I may not have spent the time that would have been beneficial to face the loss, but I increasingly understood that it was still possible to seek joy and to live with beauty and laughter and the warmth of family and friends. During our final years together, when I finally secured competent help, I began to plan limited time each day away from home doing what I enjoyed, often just being with friends.

4. Focusing on What's Best for You, Not on What Others May Think

Learning to do what was best for me and for Ady without being concerned about what others might think was an important step for me.

It is easy to feel guilt for trying to live fully. At first, I thought that I'd be judged harshly if I went to an event without Ady. To my surprise, I kept getting positive feedback. Friends and acquaintances alike kept telling me how well they thought I was handling the situation. Their encouragement helped me to get over my fear of "what others might think" and reinforced my decision to live more fully. This continued even after Ady's death.

I remember going to a concert shortly after Ady was gone. A woman who sat behind me, whose name I did not know, expressed her condolences and then said, "No one ever treated a husband as beautifully as you did."

I was so stunned that I actually blurted out, "How do you know that?"

"I've sat behind you for many years," she said. "I saw the love, the tenderness, the attentiveness to his every need. The way you looked at him. There's nothing else I had to know." She knew nothing about what I have written in these pages. Yet, later I thought that simple observation probably summed up, more than any other words, why Ady progressed as beautifully as he did and why those who knew me were happy to see that I was not folding. My time with Ady was quality time.

Not only did I stop feeling guilty for being able to laugh with friends, or for enjoying a game of tennis, but I found that friends continued to include me because I didn't have a "poor me" look when they greeted me. When they asked in a serious tone how Ady or I were doing, my answer was usually "Great!" They looked at me with disbelief, but I meant it. I am not recommending putting on a happy face or a false demeanor. Each person must react in a way that is appropriate and authentic for them. But my inner peace was real, and I'm sure it was reflected in my demeanor.

5. Getting Enough Sleep

I tried to get seven to eight hours of sleep a night. That was always particularly tough for me until very recent years, when our son read me the riot act. I always thought that I had to accomplish my agenda before I went to sleep. My son said, with great forcefulness, "Mom, I'm giving you a curfew. When you're home I want you to turn off your computer at 9:00 P.M., no matter how important what you're working on is. Get ready for bed and relax and read for a while." I realized that getting enough sleep is a conscious decision we make, and I'm feeling better and living with far more energy having followed his guidance.

6. Maintaining Adult Conversation with Friends

There is an unavoidable sadness in losing the rich adult conversation that had been such a big part of my life with Ady. But I couldn't let my life shrink to games and puzzles. That is why spending time with friends, who were involved and interesting people, was so important for me. It gave balance to my life. Even limited time with friends, or going to a cultural event, snapped me back into the adult world. Spending time with people who saw humor in life and made me laugh gave me new awareness of the healing power of laughter.

7. Acknowledging Your Own Feelings

Finding that delicate balance and staying whole was something I fought every day to maintain. Outwardly I went through the motions, but the "harsh decree" of Alzheimer's brings with it an inner sadness that never entirely goes away. Despite my many expressions of satisfaction, there were many difficult moments of coming to terms with reality. There were times that I allowed myself to face my feelings—times that wiped me out but were vital to my own well-being.

The following email to our son and daughter is an example of how even briefly sharing one's feelings with trusted listeners can be a positive step towards unburdening ourselves and facing reality. My intention when I began writing was simply to let them know that the results of my routine colonoscopy were excellent.

Hi Bonnie and Mark,

The colonoscopy could not have gone better. The prep was much easier this time. The results were NORMAL. I just

> woke up from a two-hour nap when I returned home and feel fine.
>
> However, there was an unexpected reality check. When I came back home and saw Dad, he said (as he does every time I come back from an appointment with my therapist), "How was your session?" I asked, "Sweetie, do you know where I was?" and his response was, "Sorry, dear, I don't remember." I felt an overwhelming loneliness, as I did in the waiting room today without Dad at my side, knowing that Jorge [*our occasional driver to the airport*] brought me and was coming back when I called to say I was ready. I keep telling myself how well he's doing and how well I'm doing (and I am!), but every now and then there's a powerful wake-up call that makes me face the reality of my life.
>
> Love,
> Mom

When I faced realizations or feelings like these, I found it extremely helpful to be able to verbalize them to my family or close friends. Just being able to acknowledge them in words, either verbal or written, helped to minimize the sting and intensity.

For me the very sporadic journal that I was keeping brought similar comfort. Once something is expressed, it doesn't appear to be quite so ominous.

8. Understanding Finances: A Word to Women

I know many bright women who have contributed substantially to the world, even some with advanced degrees or qualifications, who close their minds when it comes to understanding financial matters. Women have told me, "I don't understand the complicated financial world. My husband handles the finances." Though Ady was always open with me, I was one of those women who chose to leave finances up to him while I was busy "saving the world." I did join a stock club long before Ady had Alzheimer's symptoms, but my interest was more social than a desire to learn.

Then one day, even before the obvious onslaught of Alzheimer's, our son said, "Mom, you have no idea what your financial situation is—no idea what you are spending or what you can afford to spend." He was absolutely right, and I took his admonition most seriously. Ady, knowing he would soon be retiring, was totally supportive of each of us gaining more financial knowledge, and so our crash course in finances began. I intuitively understood that a course on managing money was one that I had to pass. I was merciless with my questions and not embarrassed to ask the most rudimentary ones until I felt that I understood their responses. I felt lucky that I was eased into the knowledge gradually, over a period of eight to ten years, before my understanding of financial matters became a necessity.

As Ady was aware that his comprehension was decreasing, he gradually handed over the reins to me on the monthly bank conference calls. He took a back seat on these calls long before he had to. Looking back, I understood that he retreated in order to empower me and to rescue me from the additional shock of not knowing how to handle our financial needs after he was gone. When that bank call came two weeks after Ady passed away, I began to panic until I told myself, "Relax, you've been handling these calls for two years." After he was gone, I felt his easing me into the driver's seat for financial matters was a parting gift he gave to me.

As a result of this experience, when I meet a bright forty-something woman who chooses to leave all financial matters to her husband, I get on my soapbox, telling her how crucial it is to be informed—even if her husband is threatened by her need to know. None of us can predict when a life-changing event will occur. We owe it to ourselves and our family to be prepared.

9. Learning from Others

I recommend observing friends who are dealing with loved ones who are ill, asking questions where necessary and appropriate. Here are a few of the many lessons that I learned from others:

- Distinguish between what's essential and what is not. Your time, more than ever, is extremely precious. There are many "musts," like doctor's appointments and the day-to-day care of your loved one. But other choices are optional. A friend invites you to a luncheon or a lecture. Your place of worship asks for help organizing a function. In the past you've responded positively to both obligations and events you enjoy. Now you have the gift of being able to do exactly what you want in the few spare moments you can eke out. You might prefer to take a walk or have the luxury of reading a book. You might just need to rest. The old obligations are no longer valid. There are essentials: the caregiving and all the endless details that entails. There are options: both pleasurable and obligations. Learn to ask yourself before any decision, "What do I want?" And feel free to go with your answer.
- After bad news, if at all possible, try to wait several days before making a decision. There are medical decisions that might need immediate answers. But most other important decisions, like selling a house or moving, should not be made at a time of great stress.
- Understand that you cannot be there for friends as you used to be—that no matter how pressing their problem, you may just have no energy left to help them deal with it. Accepting this was a struggle for me. Perhaps you can look for windows when you have time for a brief note or phone call. It is vital to give yourself permission to respond to your

own needs first—including your need for rest—even if that means you can't be there for them right now. True friends will understand the lack of your usual compassion.
- Occasionally, what I observed in others was a negative example. I've tried all my life not to judge others, but I became supersensitive when I observed impatient behavior towards a spouse who was slow to respond as they once did. I vowed to fiercely fight that tendency.

10. Be Clear about Your Priorities

You cannot do it all. Make conscious choices about your priorities. Give yourself permission to let some things go undone.

My nature is to be compulsive about doing things well and thoroughly. Until my need to be there so completely for Ady, my home was ready for guests most of the time. I understood early on that that was no longer possible. There were medical charts and equipment that took over the house. Ady's office was the first to go. There were piles of folders that he simply would not put away, and his desk was sky-high with papers. There were boxes covering the floor. It seemed as though if an item was out of sight, it was lost to his mind. It's not that I didn't care, but it was not worth the battle to convince him to clean it up or to let me help him. The place where I worked at home was not the disaster that his was, but it certainly was not what it had always been. All but the urgent mail piled up, and my unanswered email list kept growing. It was more important to me to exercise and do what was necessary for my own health than to be upset about a messy room.

This didn't happen haphazardly. It was a conscious decision I made to let the nonessential go. It was difficult for me, but I gave myself permission to do exactly that. As I still tend to get bogged down in nonessentials, I strive to keep that healthy perspective. No matter what stage of life we are in, I suspect every one of us would benefit from letting some things go undone.

. . .

The key message throughout this chapter is to PUT ON YOUR OWN OXYGEN MASK FIRST. Remind yourself how important your role as caregiver is and how lost your loved one would be without you steering the ship. When you take the time to nourish yourself, try to banish the guilt that tends to creep in. Airlines instruct us to take care of yourself first, so you can be there to help another. It is crucial to the well-being of both you and your loved one that you give yourself the same permission.

PART FOUR

LOOKING BACK

CHAPTER THIRTEEN

What I Have Learned

HOLOCAUST SURVIVOR VIKTOR FRANKL, IN HIS BOOK *Man's Search for Meaning,* describes the unspeakable conditions of depravity in the concentration camps, where each prisoner lived in abject fear and life was reduced to an animal's needs: food, sleep, shelter from the cold. His contention was that the ones who made it through the unimaginable hardships were those who had a purpose to live for: hope of finding a wife or a child still alive, hope of finishing a manuscript or a musical composition, hope of bearing witness to the world about the horrific nightmare they were living through, or the satisfaction of helping others. They found something beyond themselves that gave their lives meaning and kept them going. When one has reason to live, hope becomes possible.

We make our own reality. We can dread the power of the sea or plunge into it. We can long for the past or live fully in the present. We can succumb to self-pity or appreciate the goodness in our lives. We can bury ourselves in a dark hole or remember that the sun is still shining, the flowers are blooming, and there are people who care about us. We can, while feeling the pain of watching a loved one decline, still give ourselves permission to experience and embrace joy. Our reality is ours to make.

Some of the insights that follow I now realize could not have been written during or immediately after Ady's passing. Initially, I acted more on instinct than with a thought-out plan. I closely observed what was working and what was not, but it took the perspective of time and writing this book to begin to analyze and define the principles that proved effective.

Alzheimer's Symptoms versus Reactions to Those Symptoms

This book is largely about how to change what we can and accept what we cannot. The more the caregiver understands about the nature of the disease, the less difficult it will be to cope with it.

One of the most debilitating feelings for the caregiver, as you watch your loved one continue to decline, is the sense of feeling powerless. It feels like a Greek tragedy, where you know the end but there is nothing you can do to stop it.

It is crucial that we learn to distinguish between Alzheimer's symptoms and the patient's reaction to those symptoms. One is the medical symptoms of the disease itself: the loss of memory, the loss of physical and mental functions, the loss of abilities, the loss of comprehension, the loss of judgment, and the loss of the ability to plan. The other is the patient's *reactions* to those symptoms: the frustration, the anger, the mood changes, the impatience, the depression, and in some cases the violence. The patient gets angry and frustrated with the awareness of their reduced function and lashes out at those around them. It is, in no small part, the reaction to the symptoms that makes the patient so difficult to live with.

Once I understood the distinction between the medical symptoms and the patient's reaction to the loss they are experiencing, I found I was more compassionate about the first and more creative about dealing with unwanted behavior. It is exceedingly rare that the caregiver can change the symptoms, but a central message of this book is that you can change the patient's *reactions* to those symptoms by employing some of the methods described. The caregiver can have a great deal of influence over the secondary behaviors. Throughout this book, I've written about:

- The importance of acceptance.
- The importance of giving support through kindness, compassion, openness, tenderness, respect, and loving expressions.
- The importance of being there without judgement or expressions of disappointment.
- The importance of offering praise and enthusiasm for every accomplishment.
- The importance of keeping the patient mentally stimulated for most of his day.
- The importance of providing a safe, consistent, and loving environment.

Looking back, I realize that the positive results we achieved with Ady were because we removed most of the triggers that caused his frustration, resistance, and anger.

Opening Doors

In a sense, my role in Ady's life has long been to see the inherent good, to see the potential, and to open doors. In the early years of our marriage, aware that he had a passion for classical music but probably had never been to a concert, I suggested that we subscribe to a series of concerts being hosted at a local synagogue. Money was carefully budgeted, but he readily agreed. It was the beginning of a lifetime of attending all the major concert and opera series that emerged in Miami during the ensuing years. Music was the big draw that years later encouraged us to build our home in the

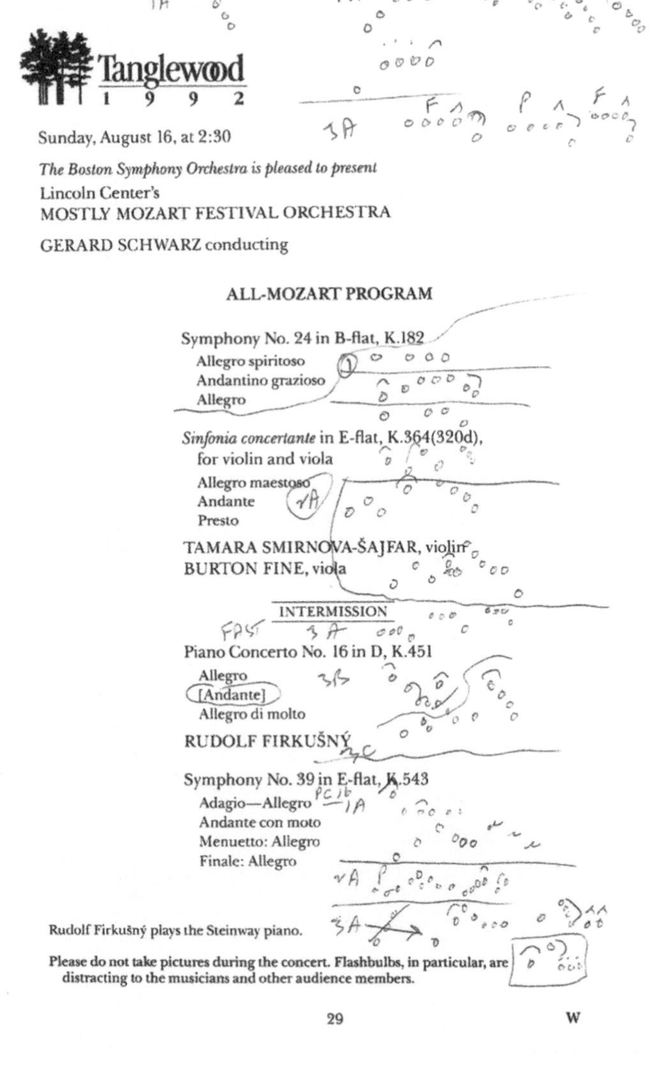

Tanglewood
1 9 9 2

Sunday, August 16, at 2:30

The Boston Symphony Orchestra is pleased to present
Lincoln Center's
MOSTLY MOZART FESTIVAL ORCHESTRA

GERARD SCHWARZ conducting

ALL-MOZART PROGRAM

Symphony No. 24 in B-flat, K.182
Allegro spiritoso
Andantino grazioso
Allegro

Sinfonia concertante in E-flat, K.364(320d), for violin and viola
Allegro maestoso
Andante
Presto

TAMARA SMIRNOVA-ŠAJFAR, violin
BURTON FINE, viola

INTERMISSION

Piano Concerto No. 16 in D, K.451
Allegro
[Andante]
Allegro di molto

RUDOLF FIRKUŠNÝ

Symphony No. 39 in E-flat, K.543
Adagio—Allegro
Andante con moto
Menuetto: Allegro
Finale: Allegro

Rudolf Firkušný plays the Steinway piano.

Please do not take pictures during the concert. Flashbulbs, in particular, are distracting to the musicians and other audience members.

29 W

Tanglewood program with Ady's musical notations

Berkshires. Tanglewood, summer home of the Boston Symphony, was the magnet. Ady would sit at the concert listening to the music he loved, sketching on the program his own scheme of the music. A musician would be appalled at the inaccuracies, but for Ady it was simply a way of helping him recall the melody.

Without realizing it, I continued to open doors for Ady during his Alzheimer's years. Fortunately, there was a lifetime of his responding positively to my suggestions. I never tried consciously to change or mold him, but to let him be more of what he already was, to give him more exposure to what he already loved. His life and mine were deeply enriched by his openness. Many new worlds opened up for Ady during his Alzheimer's years.

Building Together

Our attitude was not one of presiding over the deterioration of a human being but rather of building something *new* together, of collaborating on this complex new challenge that life had presented to us, and of putting everything we believed—and new things we learned—into effect in the process. Looking back, I began to understand that, together, Ady and I managed to construct the scaffolding of an environment that gave Ady the best chance for positive outcomes, physically, emotionally, and socially. The environment we created together allowed him to be social without taxing him or his friends. He thrived with a solid foundation of support that enabled him to function at the highest level possible.

Continuing to Create Sweet Times

I constantly strove to keep the time we had together sweet. There was a tenderness between us that was palpable. We walked emotionally in stride together as one. We were largely at peace with one another, not locked in a battle of wills. We each continued to care about the other with fullness of heart throughout the long years of Alzheimer's. My life with Ady taught me that it is possible to have gentle, sweet, and happy times even when your lifelong partner is afflicted with Alzheimer's; that two people who love each other enough can choose—even in the face of such a harsh reality—to live with contentment and joy.

Maintaining Connections with Friends

Throughout this book, I have emphasized the importance of maintaining connections with friends. Caretaking is difficult and lonely enough as it is. To cut oneself off from those who care about you is detrimental to your own emotional health. You instinctively know who is being polite and who wants the fuller version of what you're living through. I found that when I was open with what I was experiencing, friends constantly provided me with the most important knowledge, information, and guidance.

Accepting Help

I learned that the willingness to accept help from a friend is crucial. When Ady and I arrived in the ambulance at the hospital, I allowed my lifelong friend from college days to take over for me. I needed every bit of strength for the anticipated surgery and weeks that followed. When you're used to being in charge, it's hard to give up the reins, but that night in the hospital I was close to collapse. Necessity forced me to accept help. Much to my surprise, I became more willing to delegate and welcome assistance in the weeks, months, and years that followed.

Learning from Every Experience

Every experience, even a negative one, is an opportunity to learn. Certainly, I learned from my many mistakes, as I've described throughout. I also learned a multitude of important lessons from watching others—especially Lizette. I learned from my successes as well. How valuable were those medical records I had taped to our refrigerator before leaving in the ambulance! How important it was—despite my terror—to project calm and rationality to the ambulance paramedic, so he would take Ady to the hospital he needed to go to and allow me to sit in the back with my husband to keep him calm.

The Essential Role of Patient Advocates

I also learned during the month of hospitals and rehab after the final hip surgery how essential it is to have a patient advocate when one is in a hospital. Hospital personnel are universally overworked and unable to complete their work assignments in the way that they would wish. Despite the clear charts I had posted on the bulletin board in Ady's room, serious errors in medication would have occurred had I not been there. Every patient needs a personal advocate in order to emerge unscathed.

The Possibility of Regeneration

I hope that in writing this book I might help others cope with the overwhelming sense of doom that comes with the diagnosis of Alzheimer's. Alzheimer's patients today are given little or no hope for improvement. It is questionable whether the existing drugs can even slow the process of decline. In addition to memory loss, we are warned to expect a degenerating personality, inappropriate behavior, anger, depression, stubbornness, rigidity, and even violence. We are told to cope with these inevitable changes as best we can and to try to eke out a few precious minutes each day for ourselves.

The Alzheimer's Association has said clearly: "Alzheimer's is the only cause of death in the top 10 in America that cannot be prevented, cured, or even slowed." That has not been my experience. I believe my story serves as an example that, rare or not, there is at least the possibility of regeneration.

Based on both test results and his personal observations at our last appointment, four months before Ady passed away, Dr. Ranjan Duara confirmed that Ady was making vast positive strides. His cognition was far greater than it had been a few years before. He was healthy, happy, and performing tasks he had not been able to do two years earlier. The optimal conditions for regeneration—constant mental stimulation, love, appreciation, and a nurturing, conflict-free, calm environment—are not easy to obtain. Yet they are possible to aspire to and even to achieve. The profound effects of emotions on health are well documented. Stress and anger are the great killers. A growing number of medical doctors are now recommending meditation to their patients, recognizing the influence of mental equanimity on physical health.

The people around you clearly contribute, either positively or negatively, to your own mood and sense of well-being. A renowned brain scientist, Dr. Jill Bolte Taylor, documented this in a book called *My Stroke of Insight*. It describes her own personal journey through recovery from a massive stroke, so severe that she did not know what the word "mother" meant. Her book chronicles the significant insights she experienced during her long years of rehabilitation. One of her descriptions that fascinated me was her reaction to the nurses that surrounded her in the hospital. Some were rigid, harsh, and perfunctory in carrying out their tasks: too loud, too fast, too eager to get the tasks accomplished and move on. Others were kind, gentle, and soft-spoken. She shrank under the former and blossomed under the latter.

This concept struck a vital chord in me. My contention has long been that Ady's brain was regenerating because his brain was not consumed with anger and disappointment. Those emotions constrict blood vessels. Any time you think you've lost your wallet or keys, you know how rapidly your body reacts—a tightening, a cold sweat. It is well documented how deeply emotions play a part in our health. It makes perfect sense to me that the people who surround you contribute to your own mood and sense of well-being.

When our brains are not consumed with frustration, disappointment, anger, and tension, we have at least the potential for growth. Ady was always surrounded by support, understanding, approval, and respect. This, I believe, allowed healthy growth in his brain to flourish.

Focus on the Journey

Alzheimer's is a cruel disease: nothing in this book will change that. Setbacks, large and small, are inevitable, and they happen—reliably!—when we least expect them. We, as caregivers, need to maintain a balancing act, to "fight the disease, not the journey." When a setback comes, by all means take whatever spare moments you need to grieve for the loss, but never lose sight of the goal. As caregivers of a patient with Alzheimer's or another form of dementia, we will likely lose the final war—but we can win many a daily battle. This is where our hopes and motivation reside: not to change the final destination but to make the journey as rich and meaningful as possible.

Our Actions Can Make a Difference

Our roles as caregivers take a supreme commitment. It takes a conscious decision, daily reaffirmed, to tough out this difficult time—to bring every skill you have to perhaps the most important job of your life.

I referred in the first chapter to the powerfully sad thought expressed by a friend: "I wish I could do it over again." During the years of Alzheimer's, whenever I became drained or tired, I reminded myself: "Helene, you're not going to get to do this again. Give it your all!"

Looking back, knowing you gave it your all, that you did the best you could, day after day, is a supreme gift to yourself. If we are successful in our role, through the act of quality and creative caregiving, we have many rich rewards, including a deep sense of satisfaction.

The most important message I can leave you with is this: We are not automatically the hapless victims of fate. You are not powerless. Your actions can make a difference. I can offer no guarantees, as I've said repeatedly, but I can offer hope that you have a potentially vital role to play in minimizing your loved one's negative reactions to the symptoms he or she is experiencing, and in maximizing the pleasure you are still able to feel in each other's company.

Going On After a Loss

The lessons came slowly after Ady was gone. Our complicated and exhausting daily routine had come to an end. During the year after Ady passed away, I began to understand how difficult it is to overcome the void after losing not only the person you loved but the whole world you have known for most of your life. It felt like a struggle to go on, but I tried to consciously find joy every day. Ady had told me, not once, but repeatedly, "I want you to live!" He continued to shape me after he was gone. If I allowed myself to laugh with friends without feeling guilty, I felt that I did so not just with his permission but with his encouragement.

I began to look back on our years together with a new perspective. When we lose someone we love, especially after a long period of decline, we emerge a different person, with different values, different priorities, and different sensibilities. During our loved one's declining years we begin to learn to let go of what is not essential. Ady and I were able to make time only for the people who were very dear to us, people with whom we could let our hair down, with whom we could either cry or laugh, as we felt. We learned to take risks and to live without certainty. Would Ady be well enough to participate in the plans we had made? We could never predict what the next day's stumbling blocks would be. Our lives had been forever changed.

Now, after a loss, we enter a future our loved one will not share with us. After a long marriage, it can be a frightening time. For many women (as I suggested in Chapter 12) the thought of being responsible for all the financial matters is a fearsome obstacle. Fortunately for me, Ady handed those reins over to me when he understood his condition. But there are additional concerns we all have. Would I be all alone? Would married friends still include me as a single woman? Would I become a burden to my children? What meaningful activities would I fill my days with, now that my full-time responsibility was gone? Would I ever be ready for another relationship? Who would be there to give me the kind of care I gave to Ady when I need it? How should I plan for my future? These and a host of other questions confront us. It might be constructive to begin contemplating them long before a crisis arises, and to build the kind of relationships that will be there for you when you need them.

After a loss we slowly relearn how to put one foot in front of the other. Each small step becomes a triumph. I mentally marked every "first time without Ady": the first time I drove the car, the first time I went to an event without him. Of course, I had gone to events without Ady before, but now I had the painful knowledge that he would not be at home waiting for me when I returned or joining me after the intermission when we took our seats. For a long time, when I traveled to a meeting, I would automatically pick up my cell phone to let Ady know that I was safe the moment I got into the hotel. The list of firsts was endless, and each brought the inevitable tears.

I found that Ady was with me for every decision. I constantly greeted each choice with a quiet inner question, "What would Ady have me do?" And my path became clear. I began to follow the advice Ady had encouraged throughout our lives together. I began to ask myself, "What do *I* want?" Instead of choosing "have to," I began choosing "*want* to." At first, I succeeded only with the most trivial issues. As time went on, realizing that those small decisions add up to a life, I got better at determining what's best for me. Now, years after losing Ady, I am at peace—surrounded by loving family and friends, with a beautiful life to look back on and hopefully blessed with many wonderful chapters ahead.

CHAPTER FOURTEEN

The Power of Love and Dedication

THE UNEXPECTED LOSS OF ADY

I BEGAN THIS BOOK BY DESCRIBING A THANK-YOU DINNER we hosted at a Florida restaurant for the friends who had helped and supported us over the previous years. That evening, Ady wrote me his nightly letter. During that same night, Ady was struck by a fierce stomach bug, which also hit me and many of the friends who had been at the restaurant with us. His constitution could not handle it. The following morning, March 25, 2011, Ady did not awake.

The loss was so sudden and unexpected that for days I moved in a state of simultaneous numbness and focus—totally grief-stricken and exhausted, yet making one rapid-fire decision after another: calling our children and close friends, making arrangements for the funeral and for the week-long shiva (period of mourning) at our home afterwards, writing obituaries for the papers, writing my eulogy to be read by a friend at Ady's funeral, even the trivial act of choosing what to wear at the funeral.

MY DARLING WIFE, HELENE,
YOU MAKE ME SO HAPPY!
I AM SO LUCKY TO HAVE YOU.
I LOVE YOU!
Ady

3/24/11

Written the night Ady passed away

At the funeral I barely had enough presence of mind to look around or to realize who was shaking my hand or giving me a hug. The synagogue told me later that over eight hundred people turned out to celebrate Ady's life. Members of the community spoke. My closest friends spoke. My own words were read. My children spoke with poignancy, devotion, and love. Over the following months

I received almost five hundred condolence letters—most of them real, long letters, not just "sorry for your loss" notes. It was only then that I began to realize the regard with which my husband was held within the community. Ady had never been the life of the party. He was quiet and modest and never sought center stage. His close friends appreciated his goodness and depth, but I had no idea how universally he was loved and respected.

Can Love Grow During This Trying Time?

Our granddaughter, Maddy, spent a lot of time alone with us during her summers in the Berkshires when she attended various youth programs at Shakespeare & Company. Ady used to play chess with her, and she adored him.

Maddy had watched her grandfather deteriorating and saw the nonstop care that he required. She and I, too, had a wonderfully open relationship in which she seemed comfortable asking frank and penetrating questions. I always relished her openness with me. One afternoon, when her grandfather was in about his third year of Alzheimer's, as we were driving somewhere in the Berkshires, Maddy, then fifteen, asked a simple question. "Grandma, do you still love him?"

My response was immediate and perfunctory. "Of course I do!"

But Maddy's question haunted me. Yes, every night before I went to sleep and many times during the day, I told Ady, "I love you." It was clear that he thrived on my love; my telling him so was almost automatic. But a true answer to Maddy's question took many, many months to evolve. *Did I still love him?*

It was hard. Ady's need for care had increased greatly. We had charts and schedules all over the house, trying to give a sense of order to his day and to move him from point A to point B. I was getting up two or three times during the night to make sure that he used the hand urinal; otherwise, despite all the precautions of diapers and bed pads, the bed would be wet in the morning. There was Ady's constant "Yes, dear" answer to any question of mine to move him along—and yet, twenty minutes later, he'd be in the same spot.

After months of thought, I finally evolved an answer to Maddy's question that gave me a sense of honest resolution. These are the words I wrote to her:

> If one were to ask any mother if she loved her baby, when that baby, in the beginning, was a one-way street of pure giving by the mother and receiving by the infant—did she still love her baby who deprived her of sleep, who needed constant care, who depended on her for its very life, who had dirty diapers that needed changing and spit-up to clean, who filled her home with a multitude of equipment that disrupted her lovely orderly house and deprived her of the sacred gift of time? Of course, any normal mother may be tired, but love is not even a question. The love grows with every bit of care. The difference is that the mother pours in those hours and energy not necessarily with the hope of personal reward in the future, but with the supreme joy of knowing that she helped to nourish and create a person who could become a Mozart, a doctor, a teacher—a person with unlimited potential. The possibility of reward in the future makes every exhausting hour worth it.
>
> A woman dealing with a mate with Alzheimer's disease is on the opposite end of this spectrum. My rewards are not in the future, but I have successfully and happily been drawing from that account for fifty-three years. Remember the powerfully sad lines from Robert Frost's "Death of the Hired Man":

> Nothing to look forward to with hope,
> Nothing to look back on with pride.
>
> The mother with a young child has everything to look forward to with hope. I have everything to look back on with pride. A life well lived with an honorable, kind, good man, who adored me, who gave me all the support any woman could dream of, who encouraged me to become whatever I wished with no boundaries, who was respected in his own right for his accomplishments, his integrity, his smile, and his goodness—whatever I need to give now, he deserves tenfold.
>
> So, in answer to your question, Maddy, 'Do you still love him?' I can now give a more thought-out answer, which is YES, but in a different way: looking back with pride, rather than looking forward with hope. I can live with that!

That letter to Maddy was written about three years before Ady passed away. As time went on my answer deepened further. A year *after* Ady's passing, with greater insight and with the distance of time, my answer to my granddaughter would have been a little different:

Anyone who talks about caring for an Alzheimer's patient—a spouse, a parent, or a sibling—will admit that the care requires enormous dedication, and that it comes with great difficulty, sometimes even anger. I didn't really understand this when I was living through those years. What I was conscious of feeling was admiration for Ady's handling the knowledge of his decline with such grace. I was deeply appreciative of his cooperation. I felt so blessed that he seemed free of the ugly Alzheimer's symptoms I had been warned about, that he had remained rational and reachable. All these were precious gifts.

I don't know at what point I attached the word *love* to those feelings. Yet, over time, it became clearer to me that my love for

Ady during those six years not only did not diminish, it actually grew. I had such great respect for the way he handled his condition and his acceptance of all the changes in his life, for his smile, his cooperation, his concern about me, his daily encouragement for me to live fully, that I truly believe that my love for him was even deeper during those years than it had been in all the years of what had already been a very good marriage.

On December 1, 2010—Ady's eighty-first birthday and less than four months before he died—I wrote him this birthday card:

December 1, 2010

My darling ADY
HAPPY 81st BIRTHDAY!!!!!
I hope that you know how much I have loved you for
over 55 years.
I never thought that I could love you more.
But I do!!!
I have such deep respect and admiration
for the way you have accepted the changes in your life
with such grace and dignity.
Your smile lights up my world and my life.
Your goodness and caring and sweetness
and support of me remains constant.
You are the gentlest and kindest soul I have ever met
and I am so blessed to have been your wife for 55½ years.
I LOVE YOU FOREVER!!!!

Helene

Ady insisted that such letters and notes from me hang on his bathroom mirror. He read them every single day.

Ady's final concert at Tanglewood

CHAPTER FIFTEEN

Returning to Life

ON A BEAUTIFUL, CRISP FALL MORNING A YEAR AND A half after Ady's passing, I found myself at a weekend of yoga and meditation at the Kripalu Center in the Berkshires. I went reluctantly, at the invitation of a spiritual young friend. This did not feel like my world. Apparently I was not alone in my trepidation. At the opening session on a Friday evening, I walked into a small room with about twenty participants, most of whom seemed as tentative as I was. During the opening "Why are you here?" phase, one gentleman's response was, "I don't know what I'm doing here. It's my birthday, and my wife insisted that I come."

Within the first hour the leader, wondrous Megha, had us all enchanted. Her smile lit up the room and embraced us all. She set a tone of tranquility and openness to new experiences and to each other. We began by gently putting a toe into the waters and then plunged in with open hearts and minds.

We learned how to do what is called a slow meditation walk, a walk so slow that at times I lost balance. The final morning was a spectacular day. We took off our shoes and walked barefoot in the grass towards perhaps the most beautiful view in the Berkshires, overlooking the Stockbridge Bowl. I walked alone, surrounded by the indescribable beauty of the lake, the unique pungent aroma of the fall air, the vivid, glowing rusts and reds and yellows that might make even a nonbeliever feel that only a G-d or some celestial creator could achieve such overwhelming beauty.

And then the flood of tears began. Uncontrollable tears. Wrenching tears. I was struck with a life-changing insight that is still with me, an insight that seemed to come from outside of me but welled up from within. I suddenly understood that these were not tears of sadness for what I had lost, but rather tears of joy and gratitude for the blessed life that I have lived. I shared over fifty-five years with a kind, gentle, pure, giving man. Together, we had two accomplished and attentive children, four grandchildren that continue to show extraordinary potential, and many rich friendships. I have had a multifaceted and deeply fulfilling career. I was given health and vigor and a zest for life; I had the encouragement of my husband, even in the years of his illness, to continue to live fully. I never had the sense that I was sacrificing my own well-being, yet the many achievements I was blessed to have were far surpassed by the rewards of ensuring quality of life for the man that I loved until his last breath. I knew beyond doubt in that moment that if I had my life to live over again, I would make the same choices.

With red eyes, I returned to the group, who were now assembled and responding to the questions, "What did you think? What did you feel?" The first three answers all began with the same words: "I was fine until those drums began."

I turned to the woman next to me and asked, "What are they talking about?"

She responded, "Didn't you hear the drumming class?" I never heard a drum! But my world had changed during that walk. It was the moment I began to return to life. The violin within me began to sing again.

APPENDIX

Each of the following portions of letters, a small sampling of the hundreds I received after Ady's passing, testify to the amazing progress he achieved during his final years of living with Alzheimer's. They also speak of the nature of the man and his joyous spirit. They came from people in all walks of life, from musicians to college students, from doctors and lawyers to non-professionals—all beautiful friends who appreciated Ady.

How incongruous it was to be greeted at the door by the sound of Rachmaninoff's powerful, dramatic C-sharp minor Prelude—and, advancing towards the living room, to realize it was none other than Ady absolutely engrossed at the piano, playing from memory. Yes, there was musical memory and love for the beauty it represented. I was amazed at the deep well from which it emerged, overriding conventional anticipation after so many years of living with Alzheimer's.

—YEHUDA HANANI

During the last difficult years of Ady's life, he bore all his afflictions with incredible courage and grace. We have never seen anything like it in our entire lives. He was perfectly conscious of the fact that a good part of his life had ended with the onset of his mental and physical decline, but he wanted you to continue to live your life to the fullest.

We can't even count the times he told us, "I'm a happy man," and even on the bad days when his memory was cloudy, we know he always told you how much he loved you.

—Maxine & Kenny Schwartz

Ady was such a joyous person to be with. His contagious smile, his cultured background, his love of music, were all traits that he enjoyed so much and that Ady, when we were in his presence, bequeathed to us.

—Ken & Helyne Treister

Ady was one of the kindest, sweetest and most decent people we have all been blessed to know. Right up to his very last day, he lived every moment of his life to the fullest, totally devoted to his beloved wife Helene, their children and grandchildren. Ady was a gentle yet deeply principled man, whose optimism, humility, humanity and sense of personal service will always inspire all of us who had the sweet pleasure of knowing and working closely with him.

—Jacob Solomon

I don't have the words to express the feelings of sadness this news creates in me. I, as well as everyone, loved Ady very much. He had such a wonderful, kind and caring passion for everyone he met. His honesty and integrity were beyond anybody I know. He was a quiet giant of a man. He truly loved life and people, and will be missed by all.

—Al & Barbara Devereaux

Ady stood alone and perfectly exemplified all that is extraordinary. Ady possessed the very rare combination of being respected by all for his dedication as one of the community's successful business leaders as well as his equal passion for those in need in our community. If each of us were to take even one of Ady's traits to heart and in his honor and memory try to incorporate it in our day, I am certain the world would be a much kinder and more thoughtful place.

—Adam Carlin

Everyone should be blessed to know at least one magical person like Ady.

—David & Amy Pearlson

One of many letters I received from the young friends whom Ady's life touched:

I feel truly honored to have been part of Ady's life. I loved receiving an annual phone call on my birthday and subsequently solving the math problems that he would fax over. He never once forgot this ritual and I will never forget his dedication. Some of my favorite memories growing up involved spending summers at your house in the Berkshires or Passovers in Grove Isle. I cannot imagine these things without Ady there, waiting to ask me about my life with his wonderful smile or teaching me a song on the ukulele with unwavering patience. You two always made me feel like family and I will never forget his (or your) kindness.

I can clearly remember the last time that I saw Ady. We were playing board games in the dining room in the Berkshires and you brought him out to say good night to all of us. He smiled that wonderful smile again and we all felt his warmth. That moment was created by you. You knew how much we cared for him and how much he cared for us. You were there by his side the entire time. Your dedication to this man was truly beautiful. I will never forget the inspirational love that I witnessed between you two.

—Michael Berger *(no relation)*

Ady was a unique man. He had a gentleness, sweetness and kindness that all who knew him recognized. Though exceptionally bright and successful in life, he remained simple, humble, ethical and pure. Helene, we believe that the biggest factor in Ady's combatting the disease as well as he did was his relationship with you. Ady never went through the anger and diminishing feelings of disappointment in himself, because of your constant encouragement and support.

—Dr. Harry & Eileen Weinstein

Dictated in Spanish by Lizette and translated by her daughter:

I don't have the words to express how I truly feel towards you and Mr. Berger. My appreciation and gratitude for all I have received from you, but even more all the love and affection, makes me feel so comfortable and secure with you. Receiving so much tenderness, love and affection is such a natural thing from you and Mr. Berger. Besides being my boss, he was my friend, a father to me, a very honorable man who was honest, very thoughtful, with a really huge heart, humble, with a smile that could fix everything. He was unique. I will never forget his smile because it was the definition of true happiness. He adored his family. His eyes would get brighter every time he saw you. He loved you more than anything in the world. All the love you gave him completed him and made his happiness. You made him feel like the most amazing man until his last day.

—**Lizette Rodriquez**, *housekeeper for first 14 years, then chief aide for the final years of Ady's life. Written about throughout the book.*

ACKNOWLEDGMENTS

Life is about people. My life has been blessed with so many good people in it: many relatively new friends, made in the course of producing this book, together with lifelong friends who have continued to sustain me.

The extraordinary professional team that led the production of this book came into being when a brilliant woman, Judge Ellen Heller, asked how my book was coming. I answered that I had reached the stage where I needed a publisher. Ellen was then president of the American Jewish Joint Distribution Committee (JDC). She was used to making things happen. She said, "Talk to my brother-in- law. He is an attorney who specializes in publishing. His name is Zick Rubin." The book would not have come to fruition without the guidance of this extraordinary professional team:

Attorney **Zick Rubin**. Zick gave me expert legal advice and encouragement throughout the process of producing this book. Although I was new in his life, he treated me like a sister. It was Zick who gave constant guidance and recommended the following two special people.

Editor **Joel Segel**. From our very first conversation, I felt an instant rapport with Joel over common values and goals. We developed a strong mutual respect that turned into a rich friendship. Joel's keen eye and expertise constantly pointed me in the right direction: addressing what would be of most value for the reader. His insights throughout were thoughtful and intelligent. He was particularly helpful in bringing order to my vast material. His confidence in the book assured me that I had something of value to contribute. Typical of his support is the following e-mail when the manuscript was completed:

> I think I've just signed off on the most powerful chapters in the book. I can't tell you how much I believe in this project. The most precious thing you share with your readers, more than any single thing you say, is yourself: your indomitable spirit, your undying hope and high moral character, your unshakeable belief in love, goodness, and the power of ordinary people to shape their own lives for the better, even in difficult circumstances. Truly, it is a generous gift.

Joel was like a conductor who brought out the best that his orchestra had to give. The book would not have been the same without his guidance and enthusiasm.

Production manager **John Fielding Walsh** has an impressive background. He was the associate director of Harvard University Press and served the press as its design and production manager for twenty-five years. He produced thousands of new books and was the longest-serving member of its management committee. John co-founded Spring Tide Production in 2014.

Beyond these sterling credentials, he is warm, kind, accessible, supportive; and meticulous. He is more organized than anyone I've ever met. Before every phone conference with our team, he sent out a lengthy, detailed, and well-thought-out agenda for all that needed decisions at that stage. I felt as if I had won the lottery when he agreed to take me on, but it was not until working with him that I understood what a rare treasure he is.

Book designer **Steve Dyer** is a master. He came to the manuscript with outstanding credentials and decades of book-design experience and, equally important, deep sensitivity and caring. I never understood the myriad of options that go into putting print on paper, especially with the many illustrations and design elements I wanted to include: photos (some of which were pulled out of frames 60 years old), drawings, charts, letters. He was supremely patient with my thoughts and questions and always sought perfection. I relied 100% on his expert judgement and am delighted by the understated yet elegant result.

Cover designer **Paul Brown**, director of Bau-Da Design, created the book cover. We were new friends when I learned of his profession as a graphic artist. When Paul offered to do the cover, I gave him sample chapters, the title of the book, and one of Ady's drawings that I thought might be incorporated into the cover. Two days later, seeing the options before me, I literally shed a tear when I opened the one we chose, because I knew he captured so beautifully the spirit of joy I wanted to convey.

Susan Wissler, Executive Director of the Mount, home of Edith Wharton, drew on her expertise working with books and authors to review the final proofs in a most professional way.

My great appreciation and gratitude also goes to the following:

My parents, **Dr. & Mrs. Sidney & Beatrice Reiback**, though long gone, for providing the loving home in which I grew up; for the solid values they imparted; for instilling in me a great sense of wonder and appreciation of life; and for the unspoken message I received that each person has the potential to make a difference in this world.

Dr. Ellen Rees, the psychiatrist I sought when concerns about Ady's memory began to mount just before the official diagnosis. Her wisdom was like the steady rudder of a ship guiding me through the troubled waters. Her repeated warnings not to stop living, as it would be detrimental to both Ady and me, banished the feelings of guilt that would have burdened me when I felt compelled to spend time alone. During the latter years of Ady's journey, when I had the wild idea of putting all that I had learned into a book, Dr. Rees (aware of Ady's unexpected progress) persistently encouraged me to follow through. I doubt this book would have reached publication without her supportive urging to actually do it rather than writing when the mood struck me or when I had a special insight. Dr. Rees always made me feel that I had a uniquely important contribution to make to the Alzheimer's literature. I continue to seek her guidance in my new life without Ady.

Lizette Rodriguez, Ady's chief caregiver for the last two and a half years of his life and now with our family for 24 years. Her extraordinary role and wisdom is described throughout the book, and my appreciation is boundless.

Mary Hempfling, our secretary and bookkeeper, who has taken on all of Ady's responsibilities in the most meticulous way. Her crucial role is also discussed in the text.

Each of these two women has played a role they never envisioned for themselves and has grown exponentially in the process. They have also become my dearest confidants and friends.

My friends: Florida Representative **Elaine and Judge Philip Bloom.** Elaine and I met as young brides while attending Barnard College together. They followed us to Florida with their first baby and have been like family to us, enriching our lives and that of the community. **Kenny Schwartz,** who called Ady almost every day for the last ten years of his life, and his wife, **Maxine,** who has been part of our lives for the last 40 years. Also to **Helene and Tim Cohen;** Helene, with a doctorate from Harvard and a professorship for many years, took a good portion of our vacation time together this December reading the manuscript for the first time. She was able to look at it with fresh eyes and made very astute suggestions. And to our many other friends for their calls, their caring, their insisting that I join them when the activity was too much for Ady, and their continuing to include me long after Ady's passing.

Our son and daughter, **Dr. Mark Berger** and **Professor Bonnie Berger Leighton,** each highly accomplished with full careers and children at home during Ady's Alzheimer's years. Even though neither lived in the same state we did, they were fully involved with visits, deep caring, guidance, and expressing their love in countless ways. Each had a deep respect for and appreciation of their dad and emulated the example he set with lifelong scrupulously ethical behavior. They were equally supportive of me and still are there for me in every way imaginable. I continually seek and respect their wise counsel.

Our four grandchildren—**Emily** and **Madeline Berger, Alex** and **Rachel Leighton**—all had a special spot in their hearts for their grandfather and learned so much from him.

To my readers: I truly hope that this book will open new options for you: helping you approach whatever unwanted circumstances are thrust upon you with a sense of challenge rather than defeat, with optimism instead of resignation. Know that you have the potential to make a difference and that hope and even joy is often a single choice away.

Marta Neira Photography

Helene Berger has held major positions of leadership throughout her life and is known as a powerful and inspirational speaker.

In her home community of Miami, she served on the first Dade County Commission on the Status of Women and continues to serve (over forty years) on the Board of Directors and the Executive Committee of the Greater Miami Jewish Federation (GMJF). She was President of the GMJF Women's Department and President of the Miami Central Agency for Jewish Education.

On the national level, she served as the National Chair of the Jewish Education Service of North America; on the Council of Jewish Federations Board and Executive Committee (CJF), where she was National Chair of the CJF Women's Department; and for thirty years on the board of the American Jewish Joint Distribution Committee (JDC). She has spoken throughout the country, marshaling help for large and diverse groups of people with a wide array of needs.

This, her first book, was inspired by the unanticipated positive results that her husband achieved after his diagnosis of Alzheimer's. It is a comprehensive guide, combining concrete methodology of what she learned during the next six years with inspirational examples and philosophy. Although written about her experience with Alzheimer's, the guidance suggested applies to a loved one with any type of debilitating disease. It is a rare book of hope.